Coffin Bell

TWO

ISBN 978-0-578-61184-6

an anthology of dark literature

TWO

FOUNDER / EDITOR-IN-CHIEF
Tamara Burross Grisanti

SENIOR EDITOR
Tiana Coven

SHORT STORY EDITOR
Juliana Motoki

ASSISTANT EDITOR
Matthew Dube

SHORT STORY EDITOR
Madison McLoughlin

ASSISTANT EDITOR
A. Leigh

REVIEWS EDITOR
Jared Benjamin

ASSISTANT EDITOR
Desmond White

DESIGNER / ART DIRECTOR
Lindsey Turner

COVER ARTWORK BY LINDSEY TURNER

Coffin Bell *is a quarterly online journal for dark literature, publishing one print anthology annually.*

Coffin Bell: TWO *is published by* Coffin Bell Media, LLC. *Please address all correspondence to* Coffin Bell Journal,

6 Fredro Street, Buffalo, NY 14206. For more information, visit us at www.coffinbell.com, find us on Twitter as @coffin_bell,

like us on Facebook, or email us at coffinbelljournal@gmail.com. Please note that we only accept submissions

through our Submittable portal at www.coffinbell.submittable.com.

CONTENTS

CONTENTS

CONTENTS

THE LIFE CYCLE OF SHOE MAGGOTS, PLACE VALUES, & OTHER LESSONS FROM SECOND GRADE

CINDRA SPENCER

om wanted me to go to a decent school, but we were poor, so she got a library card with a fake address. It's easy to lie to the library but not a decent school. The school skeptically enrolled me off the fraudulent card, probably because at least I liked books.

When you lie to a decent school, you have to walk a long way. I had to walk alone because other kids had cars or bikes or two parents, privileges like that.

One morning, while walking to the school mom said I deserved, I saw a cat cross the road and get hit by a car. The car didn't stop. I stopped. And the cat stopped. But not the car.

It must have already been dead, but twelve pounds generates a lot of adrenaline when assaulted by a four-door sedan. It got up and darted across my KangaROOS tennis shoes and into the blackberry bushes. Mom saved up for the shoes and made me hide a dime inside the zipper, in case I ever had an emergency when walking alone. Like getting abducted. If that happened, I was supposed to escape and use the dime and call her straight away.

Its guts left a thick, dark smear across the toe of my left ROO. The cat collapsed in the blackberry bushes. We'd learned about Stranger Danger, but not what to do if a split-open cat smeared guts on your shoes. But the decent school would call mom if I was late. She'd think I was one of those abducted kids on the news, so I just kept going. Like the car.

On the way home, I checked the bushes. The cat was still there, but dead. All the way dead, no more adrenaline. Its eyes glossed open, staring out at the street, like, wait, hold on, I had things to do today. I squatted down to pet it, but it didn't feel much like a cat. It was not comforted by my touch.

Each morning and each afternoon I observed the metamorphosis of the dead cat. How its eyes went missing. How it bloated up, then sunk in, emaciated. The blackberry blossoms fell off and the berries came in, green at first, then dark and ripe and juicy.

One warm morning, a maggot crawled across the open, fleshy part of the cat. On the way home, I looked to see if the maggot was still there. It had multiplied to thousands, maybe a million. Maybe a million billion. We hadn't learned multiplications yet. Just place values. The lesson only went to ten thousand. The decent school hadn't reckoned a need to estimate maggot values exceeding ten thousand.

It was incomprehensible that, in the course of a single decent school day, the dead thing in the bushes had transformed into more maggots than cat.

I didn't want to wear my KangaROOS after that even though mom saved up for them. I fretted shoe maggots would populate out of the thick blood smear. We hadn't learned about the life cycle of shoe maggots yet. It stood to reason shoe maggots could develop just that fast, too.

I hid the KangaROOS under my bed then secretly borrowed mom's shoes and wore them to school. Her shoes were much too big and clop clop clopped. It took longer to walk to the school I deserved to attend, and even longer to walk back. I got blisters. I worried every morning and every afternoon about getting abducted and not having my dime. But, there was no danger of shoe maggots sprouting up on my feet.

I had to borrow mom's shoes in secret because she'd get upset if she knew I got cat guts on the KangaROOS she'd saved so hard for. And, I wasn't allowed in her closet anyway because guns were in there. Rifles too. But she was already at work by the time I got up for school, and still at work when I got home. She worked a split-shift. So, it was no problem to sneak her benign shoes.

The problem is that my teacher was deeply offended by them. After a week of wearing mom's shoes and preventing a decent school maggot outbreak, Mrs. Parodi had enough. When I clop

clop clopped to the pencil sharpener she grabbed my arm. She pulled me aside. She said under no uncertain terms may I wear those shoes ever again. She squeezed my arm harder and demanded to know why I didn't have shoes that fit.

In a decent school's second grade classroom, being pulled aside meant you were just a few feet from all the decent students sitting at all their decent desks. My face turned the shameful color of dead cat entrails. The decent school hadn't yet held sensitivity training on the clop-clop disruption of a bookish girl admitted off a phony library card.

Intuitively, more intuitive than a cat crossing a busy road, I knew that any explanation involving shoe maggots would not fare well. I shrugged and hid my hot entrail face behind my hair.

I told mom I didn't want to go to the decent school anymore. She argued that I deserved to go. I begged with her, explaining I only learned about Stranger Danger and place values. I didn't mention the self-study on cat decomposition. But I did tell her how I had to hide in the bathroom at lunch recess and eat my sandwiches in the stall.

Mom's split-shift job didn't promote concepts like 'present a problem, present a solution.' At mom's job, if you had a problem you went to smoke out back to bitch about it.

Mom lit up a cigarette. Damn that sucks, she said. She smoked and thought it over, inhaling, exhaling, giving my plea thorough consideration. She tapped ash into an empty tuna can and nodded, decided. She said no. She said I deserved to go to that school.

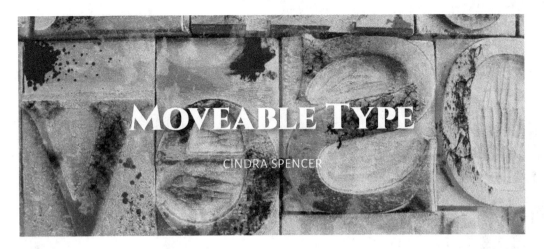

MOVEABLE TYPE

CINDRA SPENCER

e motioned for me to lie back and of course I did. A smart girl would've bolted then, made for the door. She wouldn't have got far, but still. It was the difference between a girl that was actually divergent and one that only follows Shailene on Twitter. On Thanksgiving I Paypal'd fifty bucks to Standing Rock while everyone stood in the kitchen eating the pies I baked.

You don't wear gloves? He laughed at that. He looked at me with *that* look, that one that said *Silly thing, I actually like you* and in a fleeting terrible ironic second I thought maybe he would like me enough not to hurt me.

He fastened the machine around my head. The straps were too tight and the metal buckle bit into my skin. I didn't complain in the hopes he would say *That's a good girl* again. He didn't say it.

He dropped the last letter into the press and wiped his ink-stained hands off on an ink-stained rag. The moths threw themselves against my ribcage, a useless suicide. *What the fuck is that buzzing?* He was irritated now. *Sorry, sorry.* I glanced at my wrist, bound to the table. *My Fitbit is freaking out.*

I stared up at the fluorescent light until the machine lowered and blocked my view. Each steel line of each block letter sharp as a razor, glistening with blue ink, moved ever closer.

Contact. Fear replaced by pain. Blood trickled down my temple. Cold tears mixed with the blood and made pink puddles in my ears. *He should have at least cared enough to cover my ears*, I thought. The letters cut deep into my shallow forehead, inking an impression all the way to my bone.

He released the handle and the pressure subsided. The abrupt departure made a gross sucking sound. A vacuum.

He daubed my forehead with the dirty rag and undid the buckles. I don't know what happens next. I need him to say it. I decide to ask. *So, do I just go home?* I gently touched my forehead. *I guess everybody will know now, huh?* He gave me that look again, the one that was almost fatherly, and he chuckled softly. *Sweet one, everybody else already knew.* He passed me a hand mirror.

short story

PRETTY PINK FLOWERS

CECILIA KENNEDY

rail thin mannequin looks frumpy in a sunflower smock and a ratty straw hat, so I decide to do her a favor and find a better outfit, but I'm at a complete loss and I make this discovery only after I've left her naked on the showroom floor. Nonetheless, I hold up jeans, silky blouses, and jackets in front of the naked model, but everything just looks so cheap and I feel tired, so I sit on the crumpled smock, which I've let fall to the floor. Then, I unwrap a chocolate bar from my purse. The urge to shop is gone and now, I just want to eat candy and fall asleep beneath the mannequin. In fact, I can feel my eyelids closing—my head jerking to the side as I fight sleep, but then I give up the fight and start to stretch out on the floor. When I hear the store manager ask, "Can I help you?" I realize I should just get back to shopping.

The first rack of sales clothes is near a wall of shelves filled with sweaters and pants. Hangers poke out from the rack, both at the top and at the bottom. I end up snagging my sneaker on a hook and dragging a camisole top clear across the carpet as I walk, but my eyes are drawn to the pants and sweaters on the shelves. Compared to the racks of destruction, they're neat and orderly. I don't need anything fancy. After all, I work from home, so just a few comfortable things—like pants and sweaters—could be just what I need. I unfold a pair of pants and touch the fabric with

my fingers. It's sturdy, yet soft—with a few discreet pockets that don't manage to make the hips wider. So, I buy five pairs of pants—one in each color—and five sweaters of the same style, but also in different colors. In just over three hours, I'm actually going home with clothes that are on sale and that fit. I've also had a candy bar and a three-second nap, so I've done well today.

Sinking into the softness of the comforter and mattress, I turn over and close my eyes to sleep in—truly believing it's Sunday, but the alarm goes off and I remember it's the start of the work week, so I try to remember why it is I get out of bed each day. What makes me grateful? What do I look forward to? I make a list: lunch, dinner, two beers a day, the weekend. Then, I also remember: new clothes. I get to dress in my new clothes, sit at my computer, and read student papers and give them comments for $12 an hour all the way up until lunch. Then, I can start my $10 per hour job as a customer service representative for a catalog company. Oh, the luxuries of working from home! That's the reward, right? No commute? No pressure? No "real skills needed?" I guess that's what CEOs must tell themselves when they dream up these jobs.

In the bathroom, I pull on the pants, which slide on effortlessly. I pair them with a green sweater and do another twirl in front of the full-length mirror—and I decide that yes, indeed, I had good reason to get out of bed today. Then, I see the pockets and unzip them to tuck my hands inside. My fingertips hit the edges of something folded and papery. Figuring it's just some kind of tag or tissue that comes with new clothes, fresh off the assembly line, I walk over to the trashcan and begin to let the paper fall from my fingertips, when I catch a glimpse of a brightly colored pink crayon flower drawing. When I unfold the paper, I see that it's a tiny child's drawing and the flower belongs to an entire garden of flowers. Above, the sky is blue and a few curly clouds hang in the air, letting thick drops of rain fall onto the petals. I'm not sure how I feel about my discovery. I suppose I should at least be curious as to how this drawing got into my pocket, but lots of women shop with children and shopping is boring, even for adults. I could imagine a child making a drawing and sticking it into a pants pocket, wondering which lucky adult gets to go home with a picture—and I smile. It's a sweet, sweet joke, but also a bitter one. Maybe, just maybe I could have shared a laugh or two with a clever child of my own, but the promise of finding "true love," is fading away in a daily digital routine that keeps me safely behind closed doors, escaping only once in a while to shop. I take one last look at the picture and toss it into the trash.

Once seated at my desk, I find it difficult to concentrate. Words on a screen bend and shift their shape so that I only see stems and petals. The spaces in between are pink. At lunch, I heat up my microwave meal and throw the plastic container into the trash, but when I lift the lid, I see a spot of pink inside and refuse to believe it. The child's drawing from this morning is in the trashcan upstairs in the bathroom, not here in the kitchen. But I can't resist reaching into the trashcan and retrieving the paper. Again, it's folded. Again, I unfold it and blink several times to make sure I'm seeing straight. And I can't deny what I see. It's the exact same drawing from upstairs. So, I rush to the bathroom on the second floor and check the trashcan, but the drawing is not there and it's not like I have such a complicated schedule that I can't remember what I did this morning. I know what I did. I am in my right mind. This paper—this drawing—is somehow meant just for me—and it follows me, wanting me to find it and look at it. So, I hang it on the refrigerator with a magnet, like I would do for a child of my own. Then, I get back to work.

The following morning, I look forward to wearing my second outfit. In fact, for the next three days after this one, I have something new to wear. I have no idea what I'll look forward to next week, but this one is set for now. Again, the pants slide on smoothly. Once again, I tuck my hand inside the right pocket and find another slip of paper—another child's drawing. This time, the rain that falls on the flowers is thicker, heavier, and darker. I know better than to throw it into the trash this time, so I hang it on the refrigerator with a magnet.

On the third day, the drawing I find in the pants pocket is more complex. The roots of the flowers are revealed as they grow beneath the soil. The drops of rain are still thick and heavy and dark. I place it with a magnet on the refrigerator, just beneath the first drawing I saw and I marvel at the progression—as if the child who drew these pieces were my own. If I were the mother, I'd be so proud. Every artist needs to progress or evolve—and this one is evolving.

On the fourth day, I know to reach immediately into the right-hand pocket the minute I slip on the pants—even before putting on the sweater. I have so much to look forward to now. Sure enough, my fingertips find the edges of the paper and I unfold another drawing of another garden of pink flowers, but what lies beneath, in the soil, is disturbing. There, in the soil, I see the utensils of death or perhaps a murder: a knife, duct tape, and rope—each one dripping with fresh blood. Arrows flowing from the blood seem to indicate a cycle of something—as if the blood, not the rain, were nourishing the roots.

Once the fifth morning arrives, with the sun streaming in past the edges of the curtains, I start to dread what I might find, but I rush to the closet to retrieve the last pair of pants. In the pocket, I see the drawing has evolved further—in a way I could have easily predicted, but didn't want to. My heart stops cold in my chest when I look directly beneath the soil of the pretty pink flowers. The instruments of death are still there, but the soil has layers and something remains below the knife, the duct tape, and the rope. One small body stretches out below and from the tiny mouth, she screams. A cartoon bubble speaks for her: "Dig here!"

Hanging the pictures on the refrigerator with a magnet seems so incredibly useless and irresponsible. Someone put these drawings here for me to find. I search my memory for headlines I've read or heard on the news—of people finding notes and messages inside newly bought clothes—messages that say, "Help me! I'm working against my will"—and it occurs to me that maybe I should check the labels on the pants and sweaters and find out who makes the clothes I wear. One label on both the pants and the sweaters says, "Made in the USA." Another label says, "Barbara's Sunny Creations." So, I look up the company on the internet and discover that "Barbara" is an entrepreneur who has always wanted to make clothes for "real women" and sell them in department stores. The factory, it turns out, is just a 20-minute drive from my house. So, I send Barbara an email thanking her for the pants and sweaters and for giving me a reason to get up in the morning. Then, I tell her about the drawings I found in the pants pockets and I attach a photo of the drawings that have been hanging on my refrigerator. When I finish the email and send it, I realize that the appreciation for the outfits and the drawings that I found would seem completely unrelated. It's as if I had written: "Thanks for the pants and sweaters. I love them. Here are some pictures I found in the pockets." What is Barbara supposed to do with these unrelated ideas? However, I don't have to wait long to find out. She replies right away with an invitation to meet her at her house.

Inside the stone cottage-like dwelling, etched with gingerbread trim, Barbara pours me a cup a tea from a pink-flowered teapot. Her hands shake as she serves me my drink.

"I was quite surprised to see those drawings. Did you bring them with you?" she asks.

I pull them from my purse, carefully unfold each one, and place them on the coffee table before her. Barbara's eyes glisten with tears and her lower lip quivers. She draws in a deep breath to steady herself as she speaks.

"This one," she says, as she takes the first drawing I found—the one with the garden of pink flowers and the "happier" raindrops. "This one my child, Patty drew almost ten years ago—after we got back from the Strauss Botanical Gardens. She insisted that I hang it on the refrigerator with a magnet and if I took it down for any reason, she'd put it back up again."

It's difficult for me to fully absorb what Barbara says—difficult to believe that a child's drawing, from nearly ten years ago, ended up in one of my pockets. And the look on Barbara's face— and the tears—tell me that the child, Patty, no longer exists. The message sinks in: I've been receiving the drawings of a child who is dead and has been for ten years.

"She . . . she disappeared, you know."

And Barbara goes on with a story I only partially hear, because something inside the room is competing for my attention—something like footsteps that hurry from the living room and make a loud, pounding sound as they move up to the second floor.

"Do you hear that?" I ask her.

She stops mid sentence and looks confused.

"Hear what?"

I leave the sofa where we're seated and I follow the sound up the stairs. The sound stops at the end of the hallway, near a closed door, which I open. Barbara has followed me and is explaining that I'm entering Patty's room, which she has left perfectly intact in the hopes that she would find her—that she would be returned safely—returned to her pink, frilly, flower-filled room. A tapping sound directs my attention now to the window and when I look outside below, I see a garden of pretty pink flowers.

"I planted them for her—for Patty. I wanted her to have something to look forward to," Barbara says quickly, tearlessly, immediately. And I begin to wonder about Barbara.

"You have an answer for everything, don't you?" I say.

"I beg your pardon?"

I'm just about to ask about the flowers and how they grow and what they need to survive and if the daily regimen includes things like duct tape and a small child's body, but I'm quickly pulled from my thoughts by a doll that's thrown across the room, flying on its own and hitting the wall with such force that the painted plaster splits. The lights in the room instantly flash on and off, while dresser drawers open and close loudly. Barbara resorts to hysterical screaming and crying—telling me to leave the room—the house immediately, but I can't quite hear her over the screams that rage inside my mind—screams that only I can hear. They are the pitiful cries of a little girl who asks, "Why, Mama?" And now I know. I know where to dig. ✿

short story

DUST TO DUST

GERRI R. GRAY

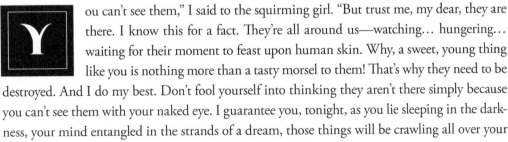

You can't see them," I said to the squirming girl. "But trust me, my dear, they are there. I know this for a fact. They're all around us—watching… hungering… waiting for their moment to feast upon human skin. Why, a sweet, young thing like you is nothing more than a tasty morsel to them! That's why they need to be destroyed. And I do my best. Don't fool yourself into thinking they aren't there simply because you can't see them with your naked eye. I guarantee you, tonight, as you lie sleeping in the darkness, your mind entangled in the strands of a dream, those things will be crawling all over your body and your pretty little face. Oh, there will be thousands, if not millions of them, feasting on your dead skin!"

The girl's watery blue eyes widened. She opened her delicate pink mouth and emitted a high-pitched shriek before running from the room, terrified.

Humming a tune to myself, I picked up my rag and can of lemon-scented furniture polish and happily resumed dusting the intricately carved antique tables and chairs that lined the walls in the great hall of the English manor house.

A few moments later, I heard loud and hurried footsteps ring out as cantankerous Mrs. Ella Strumpshaw stormed into the room, a scowl upon her perpetually unpleasant face. She marched right over to me, came to an abrupt halt, and crossed her arms. Rage flickered in her beady eyes.

"How dare you upset my granddaughter!" she hissed with caustic fury. "I will not tolerate having that young girl frightened out of her wits by you and your idiotic stories about flesh-eating monsters! Is that understood?"

"Yes, ma'am," I replied to the old harpy in my humblest sounding voice. "But begging your pardon, ma'am, they weren't idiotic monster stories that I told to the child. I was merely explaining to her the facts about dust mites. A child of her age should be made aware of such things. That is, if she's to be raised properly."

"Of all the impertinence!" thundered the old woman, as a vein on her temple pulsed violently. "Need I remind you, miss, that you are nothing more than a paid domestic servant here? You've been in my employ for less than two weeks, and in that short period of time you've demonstrated to me your insolence a number of times. You've traumatized my granddaughter—an impressionable child of refined sensibilities—upset the household on numerous occasions, and managed to unnerve the members of my Ladies Auxiliary Society with that strange behavior you exhibit. I will not tolerate strange behavior in this house!"

Feigning shame, I hung my head and noticed a thin layer of dust had formed on the floor. It appeared to be moving as though it were alive and breathing. Unable to look away from such a peculiar sight, I watched as the dust particles moved about. They seemed to be trying to spell out a message.

"Well?" Mrs. Strumpshaw asked, angrily. "What have you to say for yourself? Can you give me one good reason why I shouldn't terminate your employment? Well? Speak up, girl! I'm a busy woman and haven't got all day for dawdling housekeepers."

"I'm terribly sorry, ma'am. Please don't discharge me," I groveled, my eyes remaining fixed on the moving dust to which Mrs. Strumpshaw was clearly oblivious. "I promise to amend my ways. Honest I will. You won't have any more trouble out of me."

I glanced up and searched Mrs. Strumpshaw's gargoyle face for a reaction. I didn't think it was possible for her sourpuss features to look any sourer than they normally did; but, to my amazement, she proved me wrong. In her disgusted sounding voice, she barked out an order for me to return to my duties and then she strolled away, her persnickety nose high in the air.

After breathing a sigh of relief, my eyes returned to the floor; I could scarcely believe what I was seeing! Incredibly, the dust had formed itself into a single, six-letter word, which I knew was meant for my eyes only. Was it some kind of warning? Was it an omen of things to come? The message was all in capital letters. It said: MURDER.

It was shortly after seven-thirty that evening when I retired to my quarters to knit myself a lovely new dust cloth. I soon felt my eyelids growing heavy. With a yawn, I set my knitting on top of the small table next to my bed, burrowed underneath the covers, and switched off the light. No sooner had the blackness consumed the room, than the back of my head sank into the marshmallow softness of my pillow and I drifted off into slumber.

Being the light sleeper that I am, I was awakened by the sound of heavy, creaking footsteps crossing the floor. My eyes sprung open. I gasped. Slowly creeping toward me in the darkness was a hulking figure! Like a mad piston, my heart began to race. My chest filled with dread. My mouth opened and I attempted to unleash a scream, but no sound escaped my trembling lips. I tried to spring from the bed and make a run for it, but I was unable to move. I was paralyzed from head to toe with fear. I suddenly felt a man's hand clamp itself over my mouth.

"Shhh. Don't make a sound and I won't hurt you. Do we have a deal?"

Darkness masked the man's face, but I recognized the whispering voice. It belonged to none other than Mrs. Strumpshaw's ogre of a husband, Lyle—or 'Vile Lyle' as I surreptitiously referred to him. I could also smell the pungent odor of alcohol on his breath. Holding back my vomit, I nodded my head and he cautiously removed his hand from mouth.

"That's a good girl," he said, as though praising a dog for its obedience. "Now, I've a little proposition to make that I'm confident will benefit the both of us. But my wife must never find out. Is that understood?"

I again nodded my head, too stunned to be able to form words. By now my eyes had adjusted themselves to the dark and I could make out Mr. Strumpshaw's aesthetically unappealing face.

"It seems my wife is rather displeased with your work ethic. You apparently did or said something today that ruffled the old girl's tail feathers, and she's hellbent on having you fired." A muffled chuckle escaped his mouth. "Now, I can see to it that your housekeeping position here is a secure one... if you're nice to me."

He began to stroke my hair with his wrinkled hand. His touch made me cringe.

"If you aren't nice," he continued, "then I'm afraid I'll have no other alternative but to let my wife dismiss you. I'm sure you wouldn't want that, now would you? The choice is up to you."

Rage coursed through my veins, negating any fear I had felt up to that point. "I'd rather be fired, or even dead, than to let a vile pig like you touch my flesh! I'm sure your wife would be very interested to hear about your sordid little proposition. And don't think I won't hesitate to tell her. Now get out of this room at once before I start screaming on the top of my lungs!"

The vile one snickered. "Go right ahead. I'll simply tell her that you're mad—out of your mind. It won't take much to convince her of that. She already suspects you of lunacy and won't believe a word you say. However, the police will believe me when I tell them that I caught you trying to steal my wife's expensive jewelry."

It was at that moment I reached my breaking point. I slapped Mr. Strumpshaw across the face with all my might. He stood there for a moment, appearing stunned by my physical reaction, before returning the slap. He proceeded to rip the front of my nightgown open, exposing my breasts. I began to scream but he climbed on top of me and covered my mouth with one hand, while hurriedly unzipping his trousers with the other.

My stomach was churning from the stench of his fermented breath panting into my face. I felt so helpless… doomed. And then something snapped deep within me and I was overcome by a strange numbness. I felt as though I were hovering outside of my body, watching my fingers wrap themselves around the sharp knitting needle sitting atop my bedside table and drive it into the grunting man's eye.

As he howled with pain, I pushed him off me and he tumbled onto the floor with blood pumping out his impaled eye. I switched on the light and made a dash for the door. I suddenly felt the drunken man's hand latch onto one of my ankles and he pulled me down to join him on the floor.

"You'll pay for this, dearly, you goddamn bitch!" Mr. Strumpshaw vowed. "I'll see that you rot in prison for the rest of your life!"

I yanked the knitting needle from his eye. "You won't be seeing anything!" I cried out, plunging the needle into the bastard's other eye and then pulling it out, a warm gush of blood staining my hand.

Mr. Strumpshaw howled again and began rolling around on the floor like a man possessed, clutching at his bloody eye sockets and hurling a score of profanities and threats at me that I knew he would never carry out. I felt my fist tighten around the knitting needle, as though it had a will of its own, and I thrust it into the man's heart. It was like driving a stake into a vampire. I watched as his arms flailed and his body spasmed violently. He gasped a final breath and then he was dead.

Reality melted all around me like winter's frosty kiss when the sun's swelter brings its demise. Nothing seemed real. My mind was afloat in a dream-like haze, and I was unable to feel my feet touching the floor as I walked to the bathroom to wash the blood from my hands. I suddenly spotted a figure standing in the doorway that connected my sleeping quarters to the hallway. It was human in its shape, but not composed of flesh and bone as you or I. Rather, it was a composition of millions—perhaps even trillions—of dust mites. I stared at it, mesmerized. Without a word, this horrible creature beckoned me to follow it. I felt like I was in some sort of a hypnotic trance, and I obeyed without resistance. It led me through the dark halls and stairwells of the manor house until we arrived at the master bedroom.

Mrs. Strumpshaw was fast asleep on her king-size bed, an opened hardcover copy of *Genocide for the Masses* resting on her chest. I stealthily crept over to her bed and gathered up the book, taking great care not to wake the snoring she-beast underneath it. Well aware that the deed I was destined to carry out would most likely thwart any chances of a raise, I swung the book with all my might into Mrs. Strumpshaw's face, instantly transforming her persnickety nose into a bloody rubbish heap of shattered nasal bones, fractured cartilage, and mangled mucous membranes. Her eyes flew open and a hair-raising scream vaulted from her lungs. I immediately grabbed one of her satin-encased pillows and pushed it down over her face.

Pillows are ideal breeding grounds for dust mites. Did you know that approximately one-third of your pillow's weight contains dead skin, dust mites, and their poop? It's disgusting, but I assure you quite true.

Gasping for air, Mrs. Strumpshaw thrashed about like a fish against a hook, pounding on my arms with her fists and clawing at my flesh with those perfectly manicured fingernails of hers. The harder that old witch fought against me, the harder I mashed that shiny pillow into her face, relentless in my endeavor to put her out of her misery.

I don't remember exactly how long it took before Mrs. Strumpshaw stopped struggling. It seemed like it took forever to smother the life out of her, and I recall my hands and wrists growing tired from the constant pressure. I read somewhere that it takes the average human seven minutes to die from complete loss of oxygen intake. Mrs. Strumpshaw, however, wasn't your average person; she was rotten to the core. That kind doesn't die easily. You have to work a bit harder to put them down.

I have no clear memory of what happened after that. It's like a light bulb in my brain switched off and everything faded to black.

When the police arrived at the manor house the following morning, they were met by the smell of death. With their guns drawn, they followed a trail of smeared blood leading from the master bedroom down to the drawing room, where they found me diligently performing my daily cleaning duties as usual. I'm proud to say there wasn't a single speck of dust anywhere to be found! The officers, however, were aghast to see Mrs. Strumpshaw's disfigured and decapitated head mounted atop my dust mop's wooden handle. However did it get there, I wonder?

> It took them a little longer to find Mr. Strumpshaw's head, which had mysteriously gone missing.

It took them a little longer to find Mr. Strumpshaw's head, which had mysteriously gone missing. It was eventually located when one of the policemen, who needed to relieve his bladder, raised the lid of the toilet. As soon as I heard his horrified cry of "Oh my God!" resonate from the bathroom, I knew he had hit the jackpot!

I was arrested, jailed, and put on trial, which was given unprecedented coverage in newspapers from London to New York. The press, in their perpetual pursuit of sensationalism, dubbed me "The Killer Maid." Personally, I would have preferred something with a bit more panache—The Dust Mite Slayer Extraordinaire has a much nicer ring to it, wouldn't you agree? But I digress.

Getting back to the trial, the entire ordeal was a humiliating experience to say the least. Each day, from sun up to sun down, my assertion of innocence fell upon deaf ears; my lifetime devotion to mastering the intricacies of housekeeping impressed not a single soul in the courtroom. It soon became evident to me that everybody involved in the case—from the lawyers to the judge to the men and women of the jury—all deemed me to be insane. Insane! How absurd. The truth of the matter is that *those* people are the ones whose sanity must be questioned! I am the sanest person I've ever met.

But, nonetheless, I was sent away to an asylum to live amongst the blathering bedlamites and other pitiable wretches cast out of the so-called "normal" world. It was a dismal place, to say the least. The padded, dungeon-like room, where I was kept in the beginning, reeked of urine, vomit, and despair. Outside the locked metal door with its barred rectangular window, a seemingly endless corridor, the color of green stinkbugs, reverberated with endless sobbing, screaming, moaning and mumbling. I was forced to undergo electro-convulsive therapy, hydro-therapy, insulin coma therapy, and an array of terrifying mind-altering drugs. It was enough to drive anyone stark raving mad! Not to mention all those revolting dust particles floating about everywhere, defiantly clinging to everything in sight, mercilessly taunting me, whispering their foul obscenities in my ears.

But all that is behind me now and envelops me with a feeling of un-reality when I think back upon it. In a curious way, it's almost like the fading fragments of a hazy dream when rays of morning sunlight spill down the narrow streets of the city and furiously break through the cracks of the shutters.

A cold wind tousled my hair as I climbed the brick steps leading to the front door of the massive English Tudor mansion. My hand was reaching for the heavy iron doorknocker when something caught my eye. I paused and looked down, and that's when I spotted the newspaper lying near the door, dead leaves gathered around it. I knelt down to pick it up. A headline on its front page screamed out in bold, black letters: KILLER MAID ESCAPES ASYLUM AFTER GRISLY MURDER RAMPAGE! Below it, the subhead read: Two Doctors, Three Nurses and Security Guard Dead.

Grisly indeed, but I assure you, dear friend, it was most necessary. Dust mites are multiplying in every nook and cranny as we speak.

I've always been a huge advocate for occupational therapy. Point in case: If it had not been for my therapist thoughtfully assigning me to light housekeeping chores around the asylum, heaven only knows how long I might have remained a prisoner trapped behind those high iron gates and walls of moss-covered stone. A shot of aerosol furniture polish in the eyes to induce temporary blindness, followed by a good bashing to the side of the head with the can, works wonders in dire situations.

Whoever would have guessed that furniture polish could be so wonderfully lethal?

Accompanying the lurid news story was a large, black and white picture of yours truly—and not at all a very flattering one, I don't mind telling you. I truly wanted to spare my potential new employer any needless consternation, so as a courtesy to him, I folded up the newspaper and tucked it safely away into one of the compartments of my large handbag. It would have been very inconsiderate of me not to.

With that out of the way, I proceeded to knock on the door. A minute or two passed before the door opened partway and a bespectacled man with a graying mustache and balding head peered out at me.

"Mister Dangledown?" I enquired.

He nodded his head.

I introduced myself, using a fictitious name, of course. "I'm here to apply for the housekeeping position you have advertised in the newspaper. I'm experienced, dependable, and confident that you won't find a housekeeper more dedicated to the ongoing fight against dust than I am."

The door opened fully and the man motioned with his hand for me to enter. My footsteps echoed as I stepped into the expansive foyer. The walls were covered with brown paneling and aged tapestries, and the cold marble beneath my feet was what I envisioned the floor inside a mausoleum to be like. An antique oak table with an octagonal top stood in the middle of the room. Above it, hung a medieval-looking chandelier of black wrought iron like the sword of Damocles.

I could sense there were dust mites lurking about in the shadowy corners.

"My, what a grand old house you have here," I complimented as my eyes scanned the opulent surroundings. "And so tastefully decorated, I might add. I just adore working in these old mansions. They possess such charm and character… and copious amounts of dust. But that, of course, is the reason I'm here… to rid you of your dust problem. You might say I'm on a mission."

Mister Dangledown shut the front door and locked it. "You sound perfect for the job," he declared. "Just the type of housekeeper I've been searching for. Good help is so difficult to find, and to keep, these days! I've gone through so many housekeepers in the past few months I've lost count. You see, they just keep dying and I have to keep burying their bodies in the rose garden. It's turned into quite a cemetery out there! But it's getting to the point where I'm running out of room."

"I just adore roses," I said.

Mister Dangledown informed me that I was hired and shook my hand. That's when I noticed the dried blood underneath his fingernails. My new employer smiled at me, and I smiled back at him. I instinctively knew we were going to get along like a house on fire. ◉

ASK THE RIGHT PERSON TO GET THE RIGHT ANSWER

ANDY BETZ

He read my previous posts. He understood he required assistance. He could go to Google or a doctor or even a crime novel, but he didn't. He went to me. He commented on one of my posts. He posted his own work in hopes that I would read it. I did. It was interesting. I followed him. He followed me. He said he was a retired English teacher and could give me some pointers on grammar, spelling, and punctuation. I said I was a current college instructor and high school teacher in math, chemistry, and physics. He didn't care. I asked why. He wanted to know about when I was firefighter and cleaned crime scenes. Many people who meet me eventually want to hear a story, so I gave him one. Then another. Then another. He had an insatiable desire for details. He wanted to know how the people died and if they suffered. He wanted to know how I felt, how I reacted, and how I responded. Almost vicarious, his inquiries about my work became more frequent but not puzzling. I knew his objective. I researched his life. A small payment to a small custodian at a small company and I have all the questions to the answers he never would divulge.

He wanted to die, but he wanted to die in a very specific way.

So, under the auspices of research, I gave him what he wanted. I encountered two previous incidents involving two different people with the same problem who did not want to create additional problems for their friends or family. I didn't tell him this, I wrote it, and he read it. Even so, I swore I heard his smile grow from ear to ear. His brief reply was, "This is it". The next day, I posted the details (equipment, procedures, and timing) and he responded with a simple, "Thank you".

I found his obituary in his hometown newspaper within a week.

I feel neither remorse for him nor guilt for my actions.

The police asked me to sign my statement after I reviewed it for accuracy.

I might have, but that was their job, not mine.

FEAR IS A BUCKET BY THE RAINSPOUT

LINDA DOVE

It sits empty without weather. It learns
to wait, its metal a hole of slack.
Then it storms, and
it fills.
The sound gusts through
every odd chance.
To answer it, you find whatever words
that you must say out loud—
or die—
because the bucket has put them in you.
It turns its glare soft with water,
the blue of something big on its surface.
Its clouds, its birds, are brief.
They are tricks of the eye.
The dead bee
is real, a vain floater.
The pail holds this pollen-bit speck
against sky and damps
the buzz.
Somewhere a dance.
Somewhere soon a darkening,
moonlight
that falls on the day's accident
and strips the sodden wings
to tongues.

LOVE SHOT (FOR A)

LINDA DOVE

I once stood in England in the early morning at the edge of a wheat field full of pheasants and ate my breakfast of honey and scones alongside the man I was in love with. We were on our way to see Hadrian's Wall. The sun was gold and the wheat was gold and the honey was gold. And, so, the world was gold. I had never seen so many pheasants (ringed with those little iridescent nooses) in one place at once. I thought the birds would go on forever. I thought they would bird along the wheat beards, field after field after field—the way fields reverberate through the landscape over there like gunshots—pecking handfuls of bread into my mouth for the rest of my life. At that moment, this truth was a wafer on the tongue. But now it's twenty years later and no sweet violence to speak of.

TRANSLATION: CONTRACT • SURVIVAL

GREGORY KIMBRELL

I saw him at night. It was when he was
sick and tried opening the terrible door.

After that, he died. I felt helpless. Men
can sometimes become dogs, creatures

scared of the water. I don't know what
it is they want, drowning in the dark of

the brain. If the beast is his secret—for
the brain in fact is a beast—then I'm in

hell. He taught me a wordless language
of body fluids, of the first wine. I leave

my blood in the cage, with the key that
turns off the brain. I must eat the meat

before me, that stingless muscle. I love,
above all, the heart. I live in shadows. I

feel like I've been buried alive, covered
with water. I kiss you, Terror, father of

the blood. I can't believe the dogs ever
walked through my door. Do you have

to destroy them? Come taste my blood.
Who cares about the others, if you live?

INSIGNIFICANCE

GREGORY KIMBRELL

The eels trail behind them flowing blue tails
that shine purple under the artificial light, as
they swim through the water thickened with
gelatinized cartilage, among the skeletons of
their unidentifiable and intermingled victims.

The human prisoner suspended above them
holds with his good hand one of the bars of
his cage. The puncture wounds on his other
hand will not close, and his blood drips into
the open maws of the beasts that desire him.

He whistles what he prays to be the musical
password to the robot guardian that, despite
its believably human form, does not actually
breathe, but reveals in its glass eyes a flicker
of the spark that animates its ceramic frame.

What passes from his cracked lips, however,
is just a meaningless song. He has forgotten
too much of his dreams, and the empty hulk
stands as still as a jaguar that waits for a bird
to return to its nest and its tender hatchlings.

Now the skin of his injured hand turns clear,
and the network of blue veins conveys what
appears to be smoke up a white bone ladder
and into the lightless recesses of a body that,
for the time being, can still experience terror.

TRANSLATION: ATTACK • RATING

GREGORY KIMBRELL

My research has just begun. I'll sire the
monster. I'm the fertile stud who drips

liquid from his mouth, thick and warm.
I'm a massive smoking animal pearling

against the black hole where the young
parasites gather, sticky as calf's liver, to

burn and to abandon. It should be easy
to understand pain. I aim to be perfect,

spilling my biologic fluid in all the dark,
carefully explored recesses of the maze.

Drugs cause the hole to shut tight. But
under my fingers, I still feel a hot heart

pump. Now open your eyes. You'll see
in the mirror the pain is ebbing. It's no

longer visible. Listen. A sea of oxygen-
rich blood fills the network. The newly

patterned hematopoic bone gum clings,
like the cocoon of the silkworm, to the

blue pillars. The steaming blood smells
sweet. This couldn't possibly be wrong.

poetry

Jenny Was A Friend Of Mine

JOSH SMITH

Who's next?
Who's left…?

We are what's left of the graduating class
       of depression, dysphoria, and despair.

We hold our reunions graveside,
our fight song is "Taps."

Our suicides are not surprises;
every year is a bonus year.

We keep Mad Libs goodbye notes in our pockets
like drafts of valedictorian speeches:

      "Dear _____, I'm _____, but I can't go on.
      I didn't mean for it to end like this, but tell _____ I _____ them."

We signed Jenny's guestbook:
have a good summer, we'll be in touch soon.

She was our Most Likely to Succeed;
I suppose that held true.

Who's next?
Who's left?

Look to your side, look to your other side,
if the seats are empty—

A SPELL BEYOND TIME

CATHERINE GARBINSKY

I felt death cradled on my tongue —
a flightless promise,
an overture to grief.

Oh, I am undone:
one touch and a layer of skin slips away
like the skin of a roasted beet.

Bare against the world,
each nerve trembles.
There are no secrets now.

Vertebrae fall out of alignment,
the air crackles between bones,
radiant light shines through.

I rest upon the long hand of the clock,
listen to the murmur of rust warning against
the passage of time.

Still, when we see each other again
we pick up right where we left off.
It is still raining in Maine.

A SPELL TO BANISH PAIN FROM YOUR BODY

CATHERINE GARBINSKY

I will hold the bag of saline, I will dress your wounds
At night when you cannot sleep, let my body pull the pain from you
Let me be the poultice to draw it out
I will throw it onto the hot pavement
like a ripe pomegranate, let it break into tiny pieces
and I will gather them up and eat them
one by one

BROKEN HEARTS AND BROKEN CURSES

CATHERINE GARBINSKY

I cursed them in my sleep.
Whispering words, half conscious, small curses:
snake's venom in their breakfast cereal,
small holes in their window screens, just big enough for mosquitos to slip through,
alcohol that burned the throat,
little shards of glass on the floor (that they could never quite get rid of no matter how much they
swept) from a mug broken when we still spoke and I still thought our fights would be resolved,
an itch that they could not scratch just on the inside of their nostril,
stubbed toes on all of their hikes,
sunburns that blistered.

I cursed myself when I awoke.
Curses that broke my heart all over again:
little reminders of how worthless I'd become,
how passive and idle and full of despair,
and how dependent I still was on their approval and their kindness,
papercuts and accidental knicks with my razors,
and then ceasing shaving altogether to avoid the swirling and
spinning blood in the bath,
broken fingernails and sweaters that caught on everything,
sweaters that pilled in the armpits,
smells and stains that wouldn't come out of my clothes
no matter how often I washed them,
and tired eyes that wouldn't stop crying.

I blocked them online.
I put a sigil by my front door to keep them out.
I hung wreaths of lavender by my bed to keep my sleep peaceful,
to let go of my anger and fear.
my mother made me a necklace of rose quartz

to mend what had been broken.
I put salt on the rim of my glass to stop my tears.
I started a garden, growing nettles that stung and beautiful flowers with large thorns.
I grew my own thorns.

I remember when
the full flower moon began to wane,
and I let something new take root inside of me:
and I loved someone else.

Years later, they still try to visit me in my dreams.
They try to tear down my memories, but
my brambles keep them out.
They hacked away at them
with the carving knife I gave them before I left --
the knife I had learned to whittle with as a child,
the one I had used to make so many beautiful things --
they do not realize
it is not a weapon, and they can no longer hurt me.

flash fiction

THE FLYING HORSES

DEAN QUARRELL

eeds overtook the little park after the trolleys died. The new buses ran another way in and out of the city. The highway touched the other side of town so most picnickers went elsewhere all these years. A wanderer could find shelter in the abandoned pavilion and many did. Kids left beer bottles and more and the woods reclaimed the place. The boarded-up carousel had sunk to rot and ruin.

"I'll fix it up real good," the guy had said when he talked to the Selectmen. He talked to the Grange, talked to the KofC and to the Masons. "The kids will love it," he said. "I only need permission, and a couple hundred bucks." Nobody gave permission. Nobody gave any money. Everybody he talked to thought the guy was crazy. He railed in front of Town hall, he railed up and down the Common but no one paid attention. Finally he wandered out of town, ranting and waving his arms and kicking at the autumn leaves along the side of the road. By the first snowfall they'd all forgotten him.

In the middle of the coldest, darkest night in the heart of January a truck stopped in front of the gazebo on the Common. It sat some minutes with the cab light and the engine idling. Then it pulled out, heading out of town toward the lake. In February nights, a light shone from across the lake and a roil of clanking, whirring, buzzing noises kept the owls away from the woods.

Ice-out on the little lake was heralded by the sound of a calliope in the middle of the night before April Fools' Day. It shrieked and wheezed and chattered, then finally sighed itself to sleep. Lights came on in the houses nearest the lake, but quickly went back out again. The chat at the barber shop and checkout stand next day was unsurprised. " ...weird noises out there all winter," they said.

On Monday the calliope began moaning at dawn, and did not stop. Seven kids were absent from the Center School. The Office called their folks, who were very surprised at the news. By sundown, they hadn't returned home. Frantic calls around town revealed that twelve more kids had not come home for dinner. By eight o'clock that night the parents of nearly all the kids in town had gathered at the Meeting House, spontaneously, with no one organizing it. They just knew where to gather.

Equally spontaneously, once gathered they knew where to go, and headed up the road toward the lake and the old park, where the winter had been so noisy, and now the calliope howled. When they reached the little clearing, the Flying Horses were whirling. Each horse had a child's face, and their mouths all smiled, and their eyes all screamed.

SMOKE 'EM IF YOU GOT 'EM

TIM HANSON

He stood there and told the man, frozen in terror, that he wouldn't feel a thing. Stood there, on two legs, six feet tall, same as the man wearing underwear in whose bedroom they both stood, and assured the man in his underwear that what was about to happen to him would be painless, and would probably be accomplished in about five minutes, depending on how still and cooperative the man was. He explained that the itch the man would likely experience in a couple of hours or a couple of days, perhaps while he was taking a hot bath or shower or standing in line at Starbucks, would be intense, possibly unbearable, given the comparable sizes of the two of them. For reasons he didn't know and therefore couldn't explain, he told the man, this wasn't a typical scenario. Still, he repeated, you won't feel a thing tonight; although it wasn't exactly night, closer to morning really, but still dark. He told the man there was nothing he could do to avoid the itching, but that perhaps taking several large doses of Benadryl would mitigate the severity of the itch. He wasn't exactly certain that it would work; he'd heard good things, though. He spoke to the man in perfect Standard American English. The man liked the voice and diction of the other. Despite his horror, the man found the other's voice reassuring, like the voices of TV spokespersons touting the benefits of pharmaceuticals, the consumption of which he was told by other less reassuring voices could cause severe side-effects such as paralysis or death.

No introduction was needed really. The man recognized the other, and even knew his name: Cimex Lectularius, a name that might have belonged to a Roman soldier, perhaps the one whose spear pierced Jesus on the Cross at Golgotha. Cimex Lectalrius: he who pierces, the man mused. He made a mental note to research the topic in the morning.

Despite taking extreme precautions to keep Cimex from molesting him in his home — much as he'd done to keep the Jehova's Witnesses away — Cimex had managed to penetrate his defenses and come in anyway. What precaution had he failed to take, what detail of his defenses had he missed or omitted, the man wondered, although not out loud. Even though he had rehearsed many times what he would do and say the moment a face to face meeting with Cimex finally arrived, such as "Die you fithly bugger!", he was now in fact speechless.

Cimex Lectularius, or C.L. if one is initially inclined, clearly intended — no, perhaps that's the wrong verb – too "pathetic fallacy," the man thought, ascribing human characteristics to non-humans. Cimex was an insect, make no mistake — an insect that chain smoked cigarettes. American Spirits, in fact.

Contrary to how one would expect the man to react when an adult human-sized insect appeared in his bedroom, the first words out of the man's mouth were not "Oh god, please save me from this monster!" but "Please put out that cigarette. This is a no-smoking house."

C.L. refused. "I can smoke anywhere I please," he said.

As arrogant as he is bold, the man thought. "You enter my house, uninvited, hide out, lurk – how long have you been here anyway? — until the dark, typically undisturbed wee wee hours of the morning, and then menace me with your intention — though perhaps biological imperative or insect instinct is a better description of your behavior – to inflict a so-called painless bite, or, if I fail to cooperate and remain still, serial bites – punctures in my flesh, first injecting a salivary anesthetic and then extracting my blood — my blood! — until your, your — hunger bubble is full, then retreating into some dark crack or crevice of my home, though I can't imagine where an insect of your size could possibly hide without eventual detection (and extermination, the man thought but didn't say). The nerve!"

Cimex stood perfectly still, American Spirit dangling from his mouth, smoke curling around his head, and announced in his pharmaceutical spokesperson voice, that he did in fact "intend" to, Bela Lugosi-like, suck the man's blood until his aching hunger bubble was filled to capacity. He further explained that what happened next — defecation — was not something he intended but which would nonetheless occur, as it was a natural consequence of satiation and an act over which he had no control.

How did the man respond to that? Speaking of arrogance… Instead of rushing to his kitchen, opening the tool drawer and grasping the claw hammer that lay atop other miscellaneous DIY repair items he'd accumulated over the years, returning to the bedroom and using said claw hammer to smash C.L. to death while he had the chance — what did the man do? What did he do? He dismissed Cimex Lectularius as a figment of his imagination, a dream, a hallucination, Ekbom's syndrome…a whatever in a world of so many waking and sleeping whatevers. The man climbed back into his bed, rolled over and waited to, as he imagined, rejoin some supposed dream state from which he could then awake. He could not. Could not because he was not and had not been asleep. He had in fact been standing in his bedroom face to face with Cimex Lectularius, insect not Roman soldier, and he was somehow still alive. And at that sudden startling realization, the realization that he was not and had not been dreaming or hallucinating, his heart stopped beating.

C.L., leaning against the door frame, drawing deep on his American Spirit, must have sensed the sudden diminished production of carbon dioxide in the room, because he became alarmed and scurried to the man's bed. He immediately extinguished his cigarette and commenced CPR on the man, first with mouth-to-mouth resuscitation (the man, despite his lack of consciousness at the time, would later recall his resuscitator's foul tobacco breath and bloody saliva leaking from his mouth), and then pumping the man's chest with the heels of his hands as if he were a trained EMT. His resuscitating skills were impressive; in no time at all he had restored the man's heartbeat — and, using the man's cell phone which he located on the nightstand, he called 911. He was a hero.

Was saving the man's life an act of altruism? Did he, in fact, have a capacity for compassion not ordinarily associated with insects? No, he was too clever for any of that. What better place, he had quickly surmised when he weighed his options in the situation, than a hospital, to sate his appetite for human blood — all those bedridden, immobile, drugged, sedated, restrained hosts. Like shooting fish in a barrel. He would accompany the man to the hospital and feast forever. The only drawback to his plan that he could foresee was the ubiquitous prohibition against smoking in hospitals.

short story

YEAR OF THE VAMPIRES

GINNY FITE

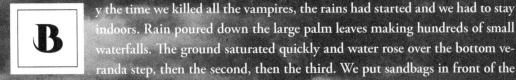

By the time we killed all the vampires, the rains had started and we had to stay indoors. Rain poured down the large palm leaves making hundreds of small waterfalls. The ground saturated quickly and water rose over the bottom veranda step, then the second, then the third. We put sandbags in front of the door sills and crossed our fingers. Snakes crawled up the walls and took refuge in the attic. We listened to them slink across the ceiling. Lizards perched atop window frames and blinked. We watched each other for pallor, lengthening canines, narrowing pupils, red-rimmed eyes. There were no symptoms.

We lived on a hill overlooking the ocean, far enough away from the mainland and the large island that the local population was small. The volcano on the next island was quiet. Earthquakes and tsunamis don't have seasons but the earth seemed calm. We told each other that was good; we didn't need anything else to happen for a long time. But we kept our extra sharpened stakes near the front and rear doors and our sterling silver daggers in our belts just in case we were wrong. Just in case we needed to run out of the house suddenly. We were still looking over our shoulders.

We made jokes, brewed tea the long way, played an endless game of Monopoly which we took to calling Monotony, read each other snatches of stories (avoiding anything bordering on horror), and agreed not to read Gone with the Wind in case Scarlett was secretly a vampire.

Preferring to be together where we could each silently count heads and make sure no one was missing, we would fall asleep at all hours lying across chairs, on the floor, sprawled on the sofa. We went to the bathroom in pairs. We had no idea how long it would take for the sense of impending doom to wear off. We weren't going anywhere until the rain stopped anyway because our old Jeep Wrangler wouldn't make it through the high water at the bottom of our hill.

Over a cup of tea on the second day of rain, I told a story about my mother walking seven miles in a fur coat to get home in a blizzard. The coat was a hand-me-down from her mother-in-law. This was before the "fur is dead" era. My mother wore it every winter for ten years until the pelts broke apart at the elbows and couldn't be sewn back together. But the story wasn't about the coat.

In that blizzard, which dumped nearly three feet of snow in eight hours, she walked from downtown Baltimore up Charles Street into Roland Park, down Northern Parkway, across Falls Road and straight out Smith. It took her six hours. She deliberately picked the classy neighborhoods to walk through, she said. Hundreds of people were walking in the streets. It looked like a scene from War and Peace, she said, a throwback to when people had to rely on their own mobility. No cars could get through, the snow was too high. Snow piled up in front of cars as people waited at the foot of hills while cars that had made a run at the hill slid back down sideways. Men yelled, "Look out, look out." People left their cars where they got stuck and the city towed thousands of them to lots under the Rt. 83 overpass downtown.

Trudging up the Roland Avenue thirty-degree incline, my mother noticed an older woman who was having trouble taking the hill. My mom walked up to the stranger, took her arm and started talking to her. The woman didn't think there was anything odd with this behavior. It was as if the snow emergency created new rules for social interaction; the old stiff rules about how to behave when you first meet someone disappeared under the first foot of snow. When they parted forty minutes later, they felt like old friends. Except that they didn't know each other's names and never saw each other again.

I had no idea why I told that story when there were so many others I could have told. But I'd stopped questioning my motives at that point.

Molly told the story of the time she was sunbathing at her apartment pool, talking to the woman in the lounger next to her about Oprah Winfrey, and periodically scanning the pool for her young son playing in the shallow end when she saw a boy floating on his belly, face down in the water. Without thinking, she catapulted from her chair, jumped into the pool and pulled the child out of the water. He sputtered and cried, but he was alive. The woman she was talking to was his mother. She grabbed her son and shook him for embarrassing her. Molly took her towel and straw bag and left the pool.

Simon told us about the time he and his mother heard screaming in the street in their neighborhood one night. It was not a common occurrence. Without thinking, he grabbed the poker from the fireplace tool rack and his mother grabbed the flashlight she kept handy in the kitchen. They left their house, locked the door behind them, and walked quickly into the street calling out, "Where are you, we're coming" as if they were superheroes and knew what they were doing.

They walked toward the screaming. No one else even opened their doors. They found a neighbor in her seventies standing weeping and shaking at the foot of the concrete stairs leading up to her townhouse, unable to move. They walked her up to the door.

Her husband of fifty years stood terrified and helpless in his living room with the front door open. "He took my purse," she said, "he shoved me when I got out of the car and he took my purse." Her husband embraced her as if she were made of glass. Simon and his mother left her there and walked home. For some reason, they didn't think about any danger they might be in.

I suppose we were looking for the roots of our bravery, about which we thought there were no earlier clues. Survival seemed to be what drove our behavior, and fury, but everyone wanted to survive. No other group on our island that we knew of organized themselves to kill the vampires. Everyone else hid and hoped for the best, hoped they wouldn't be next, and rationalized that only bad people, wild people were attacked.

The vampires arrived by boat from the big island just after sunset as if they were tourists. We didn't notice they were different from anyone else for a while except that they seemed really old, stooped, and furrowed, more like the folks you expect to spend the winter in Miami. The men wore their polyester pants pulled up high over their bellies. Their chests were concave. They wore black socks and sandals. The women's breasts sat like melons on their prominent bellies. They were loud and took photographs of themselves standing on the beach, their backs to the waves, with the moon's reflection on the ocean making a path to the horizon. They stayed in the hotel near the beach like most of the tourists and left everyone else alone.

Dan was the first person to notice something odd. Dan ran a cafe on the main road near the beach. One evening the tourist he had taken to calling Herman sat down at one of the outdoor tables and ordered a Cosmo. The guy was wearing Herman's clothes but he seemed taller, a bit younger, and he was wearing his pants at his hips. Dan said it was like having a déjà vu moment except that something was slightly off. He couldn't put his finger on it until one of the women joined Herman. She seemed to have lost twenty years. She was now lusciously curved, her hair was pulled back in a pony tail, and her skin was smooth. She winked at him. His skin crawled.

Soon after this, bodies started washing up on the beach. They had been sucked dry and resembled inner tubes with the air let out. Twelve hours in the Pacific didn't help the police identify what killed them. At first the coroner thought they were attacked while swimming in the ocean at night but there were no shark bites. Then he thought he saw man-of-war or box jelly fish stinger marks on their necks but that turned out not to be the case. The victims were mainly men in their twenties but occasionally there was one child and a woman. The killings seemed opportunistic rather than planned. Officials were baffled.

In the first week, five bodies were found. Locals were stunned and stood in groups when they came into town, talking about the deaths. The first victims were some of the surfer bums who found their way to the island every year and basically lived on the beach until they took off for the next big wave island. In the second week, there were ten more bodies. This time, they were locals, folks who worked late nights in the tourist businesses that lined the beach road.

> For whatever reason, it hadn't occurred to the vampires that if they were trying to hide the bodies, they had to haul them out beyond the reef.

By the third week, the snowbirds looked like elites on yachts in the Mediterranean—sleek, tanned, and toned. Twenty more people were dead. The sheriff was tearing out his hair trying to find the killers, because there had to be more than one lunatic to pull off this number of murders. Muttering to himself over coffee at Dinah's counter in the deli, he looked unusually pale. Dinah tried to get him to eat something, even toast, but he said his stomach hurt. Dinah patted his arm.

We figured it out a week later when Dan was killed. The night he went missing, he called me and told me about the most recent transformation of our odd tourists. "No spa is making this happen," he said. "This can't be done with plastic surgery. These people have got to be vampires." He laughed as if he had said something ludicrous. I wasn't smiling.

"The one they call Gloria came on to me this evening, wagging her tongue at me when I served her drink." He paused and I could almost hear him grinning. "You should see the boobs on this babe. They make you think of falling into a down pillow." He laughed. "I wanted to sink my face into them."

Maybe he died happy.

We went to see the sheriff the morning after Dan didn't come home from the cafe. His body was brought in by the surf a few hours later. For whatever reason, it hadn't occurred to the vampires that if they were trying to hide the bodies, they had to haul them out beyond the reef.

Dan was found by a shell hunter early in the morning when the tide was out. He looked like all the others, shrunken, diminished, except this time the victim was our friend and that made it different. We felt helpless. Our hearts burned. When we got home from identifying the body, Molly walked into the bathroom, buried her face in a towel and started screaming. The sound went on for hours. It drowned out any quiet sobbing. Her screaming spoke for us all.

When Molly came out of the bathroom, she stood in the center of the living room and said, "We have to get those fuckers. We have to kill them all."

None of us had a moment's doubt this was our mission. No one said anything about the law handling this or maybe the murderers weren't the people we thought. It was just a question of how we would do it. A quick Internet search provided the mechanics; there was even a kit we could buy. We bought ten kits, one for each of the monsters so we wouldn't run out of weapons. Simon came up with the plan. We would have to get up much earlier in the morning than normal. No one complained.

We agreed to travel together, whether we were going to get supplies or food or help keep the cafe open. There was safety in numbers, we figured. We agreed to never go outside when it was dark. We didn't even take the garbage out to the road alone.

By the time DHL delivered our kits, another twenty people had been killed. Only a few thousand people lived on our island. At this rate, the vampires would decimate the entire population. The sheriff put a bullet through his head. It was up to us. We had to act. Most shops were closed now. There was a sign on the pumps at the gas station: CREDIT CARD ONLY, PUMP YOUR OWN.

On Tuesday, we got up at 5 AM, put on our silver vests with our t-shirts over them, tucked two silver daggers in our belts, put the stakes in Dan's golf bag and loaded into the Jeep. It didn't strike us as incongruous that we were also wearing shorts and flip-flops. Fear made our mouths dry. Molly vomited over the side of the vehicle.

We got to the hotel at six. Light was beginning to glow over the mountains on the east side of the island. We needed to wait until it was fully light. At least we thought so, based on the instructions that came with the kit. We assumed our targets had been up late and would be dead to the world when we broke into their rooms. Simon wondered out loud if drinking blood gave you a hangover. We shushed him. We wanted them to be inert. We didn't want to think of them as human. What we had to do was hard enough without thinking of them as normal people.

There was no one behind the desk in the hotel. Molly used the computer to find their rooms. They were the only guests left. Maybe the sheriff should have started there. It was too late for second guessing now. They were on the top floor in the presidential suite, not that any president had ever stayed there. It seemed curious to us that with all the space in the hotel they preferred to be in one room.

We took the stairs. There were only five floors and we were young. We thought the elevator might make noise. We wanted them asleep. We imagined them sprawled across beds and sofas and divans or hanging from the ceiling. We weren't prepared for what we found.

We used the universal key card we found at the reception desk and opened the door. The blackout curtains were drawn. Simon strode across the room and pulled the curtains to the balcony open. Light flooded the rooms. There were ten vampires. They were naked. Their skin seemed to sizzle in the light. They appeared to have fallen asleep mid-orgy. Herman's penis was still in Gloria's mouth. They looked like they were teenagers again. We found four more in the bathroom in the soaking tub, their limbs entangled. They gave new meaning to the words blood lust. There were four in various positions on the king-sized bed. We were glad now that they hadn't stayed on their boat. The rocking would have pushed us over the edge. As it was, it was tough holding onto our insides.

Without talking, we flipped them over on their backs. They didn't resist at all. That information about light not being good for them must have been right. With a look at each other, we drove stakes through the hearts of the first three and then cut their heads off with the silver daggers. That took a while. Molly kept gagging. Without talking, we moved on to the next three and then the next. I killed the last one. Lightning flashed up my arm when I drove the stake through his heart. There was an astonishing amount of blood. Blood washed over our feet and sloshed up past our ankles. It sprayed on our faces and arms. It was as if the blood of all their victims poured out of them. I kept thinking that we should have worn rubber gloves, that we should have worn boots, rubber aprons, masks, goggles. What if their blood gave us AIDS?

Leaving the stakes in their hearts, we washed the daggers and our hands and faces in the bathroom. We took the elevator down, too exhausted to walk down the stairs. When we reached the pool area, we showered in our clothes in the outdoor shower meant for rinsing off sand. We stood in the sun for a while and then took another round of showers. We were waiting for something else to happen. We waited until noon. No one showed up. The real test would come at night. If there were any vampires left, they would find us.

Realizing we were ravenous, we raided the hotel kitchen, making sandwiches and taking sodas and fruit. We ate at one of the poolside tables that overlooked the ocean. Bright sun warmed skin. It was a calm day, with few clouds and a clear blue sky. The ocean sparkled.

We drove home and fell asleep in the living room where we first sat down and woke with a start at dusk. We waited without talking. Nothing happened but the regular beating of our hearts, the slow movement of blood through our veins, the inhalation and exhalation of air from our lungs. I walked into the bathroom and looked in the mirror. I looked five years younger. That afternoon, the rains started. I stood outside for a long time letting the rain wash me. ❦

short story

THE THING
WE BOTH SAW

LINDSEY TURNER

1 've told this story a hunnerd times before and no one believes me so I don't expect you to, neither. I seen it, my sister seen it too, both of us did, exactly twice. The first time, we was out there in the pasture, jumpin over cow pies. I know that probably sounds like a stupid thing to do for y'all who didn't grow up in the country, but that is what we did sometimes on sunny days when we didn't have chores to do. I musta been nine so that woulda made her six. She remembers that first time clear as day, same as me, and she would swear to it, except for she can't, on accounta her losin her voice.

Like I said, we was out there jumpin around in the pasture when somethin caught my eye. It was spring and the cows had been out to pasture all week, so the grass was low except for the milkweed, which was yellow and almost as tall as my sister. We called it milkweed because if you broke the stalk, white stuff like skim milk would come out. I tried it once and it tasted nasty. The cows wouldn't eat it so it got tall in the spring even as the grass got shorter. I remember the milkweed because out of the corner of my eye I saw somethin black against it, between the yellow of the pasture and the blue of the sky. Somethin black as night.

I did that thing where I looked a little bit with my eyes but then needed to go back real quick and look with my whole head, because what I saw didn't make no sense and my brain had a hard time believin my eyes. It was a huge black cat-lookin thing, with no tail. A bobcat, I figured. A big, black bobcat that was headin towards the woods, a hunnerd yards away, all low on its haunches like it was stalkin somethin. I had never heard my daddy or Grandmama talk about bobcats around those parts, and they had killed all kinds of other things on our land: coyotes, deer, voles, snakes, raccoons, foxes, rabbits.

My sister caught on to what I was starin at and looked herself, and when she looked, the thing looked right back at us. I felt a wave of fear wash over me as it stared right at me. I could see that its eyes were red. Not the middle of the eyes, but the outside. The part that's s'posed to be white. It stood there starin and its mouth started to open real slow, like it was smilin, but then its jaw dropped and we heard this thing scream the awfulest scream you ever heard in your life. It was high pitched and hurt my ears and my chest. But I could feel the noise tuggin at somethin in my gut too. It took my breath away and made me feel like I was fixin to puke.

Before I even realized it, I had grabbed my sister's hand and we took off for the house. I remember runnin so fast it felt like my feet weren't even touchin the ground, and somehow I managed not to step in cow shit even though I wasn't even tryin not to. It's like I was flyin or somethin. I could feel my heart just thuddin as loud as it could inside my chest. I felt like surely this thing had took off after me when it saw me startin to run but I was too scared to look back to make sure.

The house was in my sights at that point but felt like it was miles away. I could see the barb-wire fence gettin closer. My sister was cryin and wailin and not able to keep up runnin, so I picked her up and slung her round my waist. She saw behind me, looked right at what I had been too afraid to look back at, and screamed as loud as she could, shakin like she was havin a seizure, and started clawin at my skin, aimin to climb on top of my head. She scratched up my left ear pretty good. You can still see the scars.

I trucked it as fast as I could and tossed her over the fence and slid under it, smooth as I could, like I had practiced in baseball, picked her right back up off the ground, and kept goin. Somethin hit the fence a beat behind me, and I heard another awful scream, this one with this sharp heat that blew at my back and carried an awful stench with it. We busted up into the house and slammed the door behind us, locked both locks, and ran into Mama and Daddy's bedroom, where we jumped up onto the bed and got under the covers, shakin and whinin like a couple of scared dogs.

Mama came in there and asked us what in the world was goin on. We were out of breath and my sister's eyes were wide and she just kept shakin her head back and forth. I felt like my heart was gon' burn a hole in my chest, it was beatin so fast. We told her that somethin had got after us out in the pasture, somethin like we had never seen before, and she took off to the back door to have a look out the window. There was nothin there, far as she could see. She grabbed the shotgun and walked out to the fence to check it for fur or feathers or whatever. She didn't see a damn thing. We looked out window and didn't see nothin neither.

Later that night, as I was tryin to fall asleep, I felt the back of my head and noticed that some of the hairs at the nape of my neck had been singed.

As you might imagine, I was awful leery of goin out in the pasture after that. My sister didn't much want to have anything to do with the outdoors at all anymore, so she tended to stay inside. She was hoarse from screamin, but still managed to tell Ms. Petty, her teacher at school, what we had seen. Ms. Petty had told her that we did have bobcats in our part of the world. She said black ones were real rare but that they were real. That put us at ease a little bit, even if we weren't too thrilled to have been chased by one.

That next spring Grandmama came to live with us. It wasn't too much different from before because she had always just lived on the other side of the pasture from us and was always at our house anyway, but it was upsettin to see her so sad and confused all the time. Daddy said she had a brain disease where she was losin all her memories and would forget how to take care of herself. All her brothers and sisters had died a long time ago, most of them when they were kids, so we had to take care of her, Daddy said.

She would say some of the craziest shit to us. Like this one time at dinner, when I was goin round the table and puttin mashed taters on everybody's plate. I got to her and she looked me in the eye and said, "Your great-grandfather was a demon." That was her talkin about her own father, the man who had bought and cleared and farmed our land, the man who had given us all his name! I swear to God, that's what she said to me. Everybody just stood there and stared at her, not sure what to do. "He's a demon and he's tryin to bring somebody back to Hell with him."

Daddy tried to shush her but she started yellin over him and thrashin around. Mama took my sister out of the room and I held Grandmama's arms to her side while Daddy pushed two pills down her throat, held her mouth closed, and stroked her throat so she'd swallow, like I had seen him to do the dogs when they needed to be wormed. She calmed down and passed out sittin there at the table. We had dinner around her and nobody said a word.

Over time I forgot how scared I had felt that day with the bobcat, and I started to venture back out into the pasture and the woods again. We owned a lot of land back then and Daddy had started teachin me how to hunt. I didn't feel any fear when I was out in the woods with him. My Daddy was a big man with skin dark from spendin all his days in the sun. He took me to the deer stand he had built near the gravel pit, and told me it was the best place on our land to get a deer.

As we were walkin to the deer stand, I noticed somethin big and yellow peekin out from behind a big clump of brambles and weeds. "That's a school bus," Daddy told me. "Somebody used to live in it." That was the coolest thing I'd ever heard. I went over to have a look and Daddy told me to be careful and not get too close. He and Grandmama had stored a bunch of barrels of old farm chemicals in the bus, and he didn't want me near 'em. But I had to get closer. I could see ratty curtains hangin from the windows, and half a dozen candles melted on the dashboard. The bus was filthy and halfway covered up in that mossy stuff that grows on the side of trees and looks like bark but ain't. I took a step back and hollered when I got caught on somethin. It was thorns from a yellow rose bush growin in the mess of weeds.

I asked Daddy who lived there and he said he didn't know. "How come you don't know who lived in a bus in your own back yard?" I asked him and he shot me a dirty look. "Boy, this ain't your back yard and don't you ever forget it. This is the woods and the woods is wild."

We found the deer stand and only sat up there for half an hour, felt like, before the biggest buck I ever saw wandered up. Daddy let me have the first shot at it but I got nervous and my gun kicked and I missed. The buck took off but Daddy was a good shot and brought him down easy. We had venison steaks the next night and venison stew the night after that.

After dinner, when Mama was cleanin up and Daddy went outside to smoke, I asked Grandmama, "Who lived up in that old school bus out near the gravel pit?" Grandmama had barely been awake through dinner. We had learned to give her a pill before dinner or else have to sit through some awfully weird shit. But I knew she knew somethin Daddy wasn't tellin me so I had to ask. Childish curiosity and all that.

"Your great-grandfather was a demon," she told me, just like she had before. She looked me right in the eye and she said: "Mother loved him but couldn't have him in the house because the babies kept dyin."

Just then I realized that my sister was in the doorway listenin. She got scared and ran off to tell Mama, who came stormin in and shooed me away.

That night my sister woke up screamin and hollerin like she was bein murdered. She woke the whole damn house! Mama and Daddy came runnin into our room and askin me what happened, even though I was barely awake myself. "You're havin a nightmare, you're havin a nightmare!" they told her over and over to calm her down. She finally hushed her cryin and told us that in her dream she had been buried alive, and had tried climbin out, but there were thorny vines wrapped all around her legs tryin to pull her back down.

Mama lifted up her nightgown and there were awful scratches all over my sister's legs. Mama looked at me as if to ask what I knew about how they got there but I could only shake my head.

"One more to go and then he'll leave us be," said Grandmama, who had apparently been listenin in from the doorway without any of us noticin.

That upset Daddy and he asked her what the hell she meant by that.

Grandmama stood there and looked up toward the ceilin, like she was listenin for somethin. Then she started to whisper: "Eleven souls to feast on, a bounty well arranged. The devil seeks another and the demon will be changed."

Mama had to hold Daddy back. He looked like he wanted to tackle his own mama. He started yellin about how he couldn't take hearin about demons all the time from her and how she was givin my sister nightmares, and why couldn't she just go on and die if she was goin to spend all her time in his house talkin bout the devil while her brain rotted away. Grandmama just kept starin at the ceilin, listenin. My sister was back to cryin at this point and my Mama started rockin her like a baby.

"One more and then he'll leave us," Grandmama repeated, and she lifted her hand real slow and pointed. She pointed right at my sister.

Daddy let me go out huntin on my own when I turned twelve. By then he and I had been in the woods enough for me to have lost my fear, or so I tried to believe. My Daddy wasn't scared of nothin, far as I could tell, so I tried real hard to carry myself the same way in case fake courage could turn into real.

It was after Thanksgivin and we were out of school. I woke up real early, before the sun came up, and kissed my sister on the forehead before tip-toin out of the room. I had got my gun and pack set up and ready the night before so all I'd have to do was grab and go. The moon was still out and it was fat and full and bright as hell which made it real easy to make my way over the fence and out into the pasture and to the woods. Everything was lined in this strange blue, like from some other world, and it was pretty to look at but put me a little on edge, on accounta it not bein a color you see very much in the world, just in picture books.

I knew the moon wouldn't be much use to me as soon as I got to the stand. See, deers know better than to be out and about in a full moon. They ain't stupid, they spend a full moon ruttin and hidin, not tryin to be out and gettin caught in the bright light. But I'd been plannin my first solo hunt for a while and I knew I needed to just get it behind me, fat moon or no fat moon, so I just kept walkin.

When I came up on the school bus, my heart started poundin. What all had been growin up around the bus was dead now, turned black. All except the yellow roses, which were fully in bloom and climbin up and around the sides of that nasty bus. I looked straight ahead and just kept walkin. I had a shotgun in my hands and that made me feel more brave than I would have felt empty-handed, for sure, but without my Daddy there with me, my heart was goin wild. I tried to talk myself up — "Scared of a goddamn school bus, boy? Is you scared of them roses too?" — I said to myself, my words makin clouds in the cold. I set my jaw and wrinkled up my face in the meanest look I could conjure and kept walkin until I got to that deer stand, which was really just seven little pieces of wood nailed to a tree to make a ladder, and half a dozen bigger pieces wedged between two big branches, really just big enough for one person. Well, one person or Daddy with me as a kid, I guess.

I settled in and tried to get comfortable so my feet wouldn't fall asleep. I had learned the hard way what happens if you let any of your limbs go numb and need to move when you really need to be still as possible. The woods were quiet except for the wind. It kicked up and died down. I

> **What all had been growin up around the bus was dead now, turned black. All except the yellow roses, which were fully in bloom.**

figured maybe it was a trick of the moonlight but it looked like the wind and the leaves in the trees were not quite synced up. The wind would kick up one way but the leaves would seem to go the other way or not go at all. I thought maybe I was still tired and my brain wasn't up for handlin all the information comin at that early hour.

I didn't remember to bring a watch so it's hard to say how long I sat there before I fell asleep. When I woke up, the first thing I noticed was the light. It had changed from a silvery blue to a strange yellow. I reckoned because the sun was comin up and crowdin out the moon. I felt around for my pack and realized it had fallen to the ground while I slept. I said a cuss word that would have gotten me in trouble if Mama had heard it. I was fixin to head down the ladder when I saw the black thing.

It was standin fifty feet away and it was sniffin the base of an oak tree. I flashed back to that day in the pasture years ago when fear had taken over and sent me boltin toward the house, but my mind snapped back when I realized it wasn't the black bobcat at all; it was a black deer. It was fully grown, long and muscled, with a big eight-point rack. I had never seen or heard of a black deer. Its antlers looked to be a strange shade of this dark reddish blue, nearly the color of a real bad bruise. I thought no one would ever believe me if I told them I had seen a black deer, so I had to bring this'n down and get a trophy out of it. I thought about how Daddy would mount the rack right in the livin room, he'd be so proud.

I brought the shotgun up to my eye as slow and careful as I could, but the wood under me shifted and creaked. The deer snapped its head up and looked right into my eyes. Its eyes, where they were meant to be white, were red. I started thinkin "what the—" when this thing spread its lips out into a smile and I could see its teeth. They were all crooked and spaced out. Its jaw dropped and it let loose a scream, the same scream that I had heard come from that bobcat. Then, and I know how unbelievable this sounds, but I swear to God, that thing stood up on its hind legs while it was screamin and kept lookin right at me the whole time. Screamin and standin up. It had to be ten feet tall. My mind felt … I don't know … scrambled and my heart was hurtin and I thought I was fixin to go crazy, right there on that deer stand, but somehow I managed to get my shit together enough to pull the trigger. I watched that thing fall to the ground and I went on autopilot. I dropped outta that deer stand quicker than a jet plane takes off and ran fast as God would carry me. The house was about a mile and a half from the deer stand so I knew I had a haul ahead of me.

I felt light on my feet but it was sort of hard to run with the gun in my hands. I wasn't about to give it up, though, long as I could hang on to it and still keep movin. I honestly thought I had killed the thing until I heard what sounded like thunder behind me and inside my head. I couldn't tell if it was my heart beatin or what. When I hit a clearin, I summoned the courage to twist my head just enough to glance behind me and what was comin for me, and I quickly realized that what felt like thunder was actually the rumble of hooves behind me, as the black deer was after me, its red eyes weepin and its nostrils flarin and spewin snot ever'which way. But I swear when I looked behind me it looked more like ten or twelve black deer runnin after me.

The sight of that caused me to run so fast that I think I took years off my life. I couldn't really process what I was seein at the time, but I swear when I passed the clearin near the school bus, I saw a circle of fresh dirt surroundin the bus, and them yellow roses from the bush — I don't know how many, there wasn't no time to count — were spread out along the circle. The black deer screeched at the back of my head as we passed, and I could feel its breath on me, scaldin hot, at the base of my skull. At that point I knew I had to do somethin to buy some time so I chucked my gun round my waist in the hopes that it would trip the beast up. Sure enough I heard a stumble and a snort and a scream and that gave me the push I needed to top the hill and sprint through the pasture, over the barb-wire fence, and toward the back porch, where my little sister was standin and watchin, her eyes wide open and her hands mufflin her own screams. I tackled her and we collapsed into the door and slammed it shut behind us, and scrambled to move away from the door just as we saw Grandmama come up the hall — runnin almost, faster than I ever saw her move — and open the damn door. We screamed "NO!" but it was too late, she had already flung it open. We saw what looked like a burst of wind hit her and knock her to the floor. She screamed a scream that made my heart hurt and my guts twitch. Then the wind seemed to suck back out of the house and the door slammed shut by itself.

My sister and me crawled over to Grandmama. She was lyin there with her eyes wide open. They was red, in the parts that ought to have been white. She wasn't breathin and she wouldn't ever again. My sister looked out the window and saw a yellow rose on the porch.

Mama and Daddy sold our family's land not long after and we moved here. Our house hardly has a yard at all, and there's no woods anywhere near us. Daddy got a job at the manufacturin plant and makes enough money that Mama can stay home and work in the flowerbed most days and take us to school and back.

My sister lost her voice from screamin so hard that mornin when she saw me comin back from the deer stand. She ain't been able to talk at full volume since, even when she wants to. So I am the one who always has to tell this story when people ask how she lost her voice. Which is a lot. And ain't nobody who believes it in the end. I don't expect you'll be any different. ❧

BEGIN AT NIGHT

BENJAMIN BRINDISE

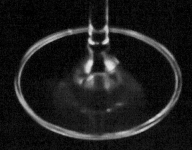

A bottle of wine. Two chairs. Two glasses. One for him, and one for her. Roger at the Village Merchant had suggested a new brand of Riesling, but Oliver chose the 14 Hands like he always did. It was her favorite.

Work had been busy for both of them as it got to be for most people eventually. Time went the way it did, slipping and sliding over the horizon without a fuss. Tonight was to make up for it. Tonight was for something special.

Their two-bedroom apartment was small, but they'd always managed. The kitchen was a nook, or as Oliver put it: a literal hole in the wall. So they turned the living room into half a dining room as well, but tonight wasn't for eating in front of the TV. Before leaving for work, Oliver emptied one of the bedrooms and in the middle set their small, circular table.

His heart matched his feet, beating against the sidewalk as he made his way home. It had been so long since they'd had real time together. Sometimes when that happens, the bridge between hearts can get lost in a fog until you start to forget it was ever there. Moss can over grow it; make it look foreign by the time the fog clears.

He felt jumper cables on his ventricles—something live traveling through them. It had been so long he'd forgotten the last time he'd felt this way. Maybe the day he met her. Yet here it was again.

Oliver held the list out in front of him, his bag of stuff under one arm. He looked it down and made sure he had everything. Check, check, check. His eyes flitted down the instructions.

1.) Begin at Night

Oliver shoved the list back in his pocket and got on his way.

When Oliver got home he checked the apartment for anything that wasn't supposed to be there. No spiders. No flies. No mice scuttling through the baseboard. When he was satisfied he turned off all the other lights in the apartment and went to the bedroom with the table in it and closed the door behind him.

He set the two wine glasses on opposite sides of the table in front of the chairs and placed a candle in the center between them. Next to it he deposited a box of matches and the bottle of wine. He checked his watch. The sun was supposed to set in twenty minutes. His face grew red with the thought of her being home so soon.

With nothing to do but wait Oliver pulled the list back out of his pocket and triple-checked. Everything was as it was supposed to be.

He reread the disclaimers. Follow these instructions to the tee. If anything does not go according to the instructions, abandon immediately.

When the shadows in the room grew longer he got up and went to the bedroom window and grabbed the inner edges of the curtains. His fingers made them tremble. Outside things were the way they'd always been. The sun sat fat and orange in the evening sky as it sluggishly disappeared behind the horizon. People bustled along the block below. He looked out for a moment longer and then pulled the curtains shut.

Then he crossed the room, turned the lights off and locked the door. The room was dark now. Somehow it felt bigger. Like there were more corners. He sat back down and tried to ignore it. He picked up the wine bottle, pulled out the cork, and poured two glasses.

He grabbed the matches at the center of the table and pulled one out. In the dark the candle and the bottle of wine could almost pass for each other. He tapped the match head against the rough pattern on the box and the tick-tick sound it made was closer to the clock dial winding down on a time bomb. He struck the match anyway and watched the angry flare throw light around the room before it calmed down.

Light glinted off the unoccupied wine glass across from him. If this was going to work he was supposed to stay focused, but the memory it brought him was too strong. It overwhelmed him the way smelling salts will open the eyes of a sleeping man and there she was again. Like a skipping record finally coming unstuck. The light glinted off the ring he'd just slipped onto her finger.

His eyes flitted to the wedding pictures on the wall. The candlelight danced on their glass frames, too. His eyes fell back to the unoccupied glass.

He went over the list in his head.

- Set the table.
- Seal the curtains.
- Turn off the lights.
- Lock the door.
- Pour the wine.
- Light the candle.
- Make a toast and take a sip.

He closed his eyes for a moment and then swallowed hard. When he opened his eyes he grabbed the wine glass in one fluid motion and lifted it up to the center of the table.

"To you, Elizabeth. To never really being gone," he paused for a moment and then added, "And to coming back."

Oliver brought the glass to his lips. His tongue caught the wine. When he lowered his glass things were different. There was something else in the room. His chest turned to a pistoning engine that generated cold instead of heat. His skin went sweat shined as if he was just coming down with a case of something common and unpleasant.

He focused on the script. "Say aloud the words, 'I wish to parley with you.' Listen carefully. If the presence agrees, ask a question. If they wish to continue they will ask you one in return. You must answer each question truthfully; however you do not have to answer each question fully or completely. Guard you secrets, for giving them up could result in disaster."

"I—I wish to parley with you."

For a long time nothing happened. The script said to shut down the ritual if there was no response, but he couldn't accept that as the result. He had tried prayer, a séance, gone to a psychic. None of it had worked. This was the last chance and deep in his heart, down in the gravel-ridden soil of it, there was an insistence that long ago convinced him their time wasn't over yet.

The shadows in the chair moved suddenly. They swirled like smoke caught in a glass tube. From across the table came one word: ask.

He licked his lips and wished for water. Despite the chill on his skin the room felt warm.

"Is it really you?"

The swirl again. It was taking on a form he couldn't recognize yet.

"It is, Ollie." The words came like a rustle of leaves, toward him and then behind him and away. She was the only person he'd ever let call him that.

"What would you do to see me again?" came back across the table. His mind was a bouquet of neon flowers that lit up the darkest corners of his consciousness. After everything she was here.

She was back. Without thinking he responded.

"Anything."

The swirl picked up speed.

"Where have you been?"

"Where all things end up. Between the cracks."

He almost disrupted the order, which the script said was a very big mistake. There had to be more to the answer than that. His mouth opened to speak, but her question came first.

"Have you missed me?"

The bottoms of his eyes blurred as they began to fill.

"I think about you every minute of every day. I try to hear you laugh in my head, but it's never the same. When you went, it felt like whatever heart the world had was gone. Everything feels so empty without you here. I feel so empty without you here."

He wiped tears from his cheek and swallowed hard again. He looked away as if to hide his crying from someone. When he did she was the light coming in from beneath the curtains. The script came back to him. He'd forgotten a step. He was supposed to seal the window so no light came through. What he saw leaking from the edges was an ashy blue; dingy, but somehow glowing and alive. In his confusion a thought occurred to him: it looks the way you've felt this whole time. When he looked back the swirling had taken a shape. A spiral. Wide at the edges, pulling to small curves until it pin pricked at the middle.

"Can I make you stay?"

The spiral circled faster. He had a hard time looking from it.

"Yes," from across the table. "Are you willing to do what it takes?"

"Yes," he said with no hesitation. The script came to him again. He was supposed to sip the wine after every question, but his glass was still full. Across the table he noticed the glass was half empty. But it's still working. Must not be an exact science.

"What do I have to do?"

From across the table the answer came. Oliver's face didn't change. He merely nodded. The spiral spun so fast it looked like a pinwheel in a hurricane. Barely more than a blur.

Even though the script said not to stray from the ritual—that changing anything at all could have dire consequences, that opening something didn't mean you'd know what came through it—Oliver stood up from the table, unlocked the door, and walked to the butcher's block on the kitchen counter. He pulled the largest blade from it. Then he walked to the front door and out into the hallway of the apartment building.

Minutes later there were knocks on doors. After that there was a scream.

The thing across the table that was not Elizabeth laughed and poured itself another glass of wine. ❧

creative nonfiction

DEATH ALSO OFFERS GUIDED TOURS

ALEX KAZEMI

For something that is as inevitable a part of their life as their birth, humans seem to have become very bad at dying. Always preferring to look the other way, treading unsteadily backwards whilst time moves steadily forwards. They think that under the bright white light of the hospital room and with the clear potions that flow into their veins they will cheat it somehow. That it is an offer they can turn down. I wonder why.

So as you were asking, I suppose I could show you how to get into the Underworld to have a look around for yourself. If you chose you could do what I have done and watch people die over and over and learn how to get there on your own. I can show you the route, however, should you decide that business is really not for you, thank you very much. I will tell you about some things we might learn on the way.

I am a guide, someone who accompanies the deceased to the afterlife, so I know all the hidden entrances. The old word for my kind was psychopomp. The name sounds silly dropped into modern conversation, but this is all that it means in translation – guide of souls. In older times, they made stories of us on cold, moonless nights. The guide might be in any of a number of forms – an ancient god with winged feet and a bag of tricks, a blinding angel wreathed in fire or a black raven sitting quietly on a branch looking at you with one eye. Or someone earthlier still – a doctor, say, in a white coat on which you perhaps notice the small drop of blood on the sleeve. If you wanted to learn to be such a guide then you must also learn not to judge the souls you take. That really is not part of the job.

You will need a gold coin as payment. Any one will do but don't bother coming without one because you will end up stuck on the bank of the last river for at least a hundred years. And I don't have any restaurant recommendations for that particular part of purgatory.

I wonder what interest you have in these matters then?

It might be that you are trying to find a certain person to tell them the words you should have spoken whilst they were still alive.

It might be that you desperately want to bring that same person back because you miss them.

It might be that you want to hear portents of your future and when you might die yourself, because they say that the dead have that power of foretelling.

Or it might just be that you are curious in a kind of creepy rich tourist way.

We will use one particular entrance but there are many others. We will find the River Acheron in north-western Greece and follow it into one of its underground caverns. And I know what you are thinking. Isn't it the River Styx? But it turns out it is more complex than that and there are five rivers in the Underworld and actually it is mostly said to be the Acheron where Charon rows. When you look at photographs of it in the travel brochures it will look green and cool and inviting, such that you can picture its waters drifting languidly amongst the trees. You will be thinking it doesn't seem that bad. I will show you the black lake in the cavern it flows into and the distant island across its waters. It is possible you might not find it so inviting then.

But let's keep going because there are other interesting things to see.

By the way don't go on one of those cheaper tours that take you to the Necromanteion, an old building on a cliff above the Acheron. You will say it is just ruins. That is now true. It used to be sold as a way to enter the Underworld. Except the ancient priests would take your money, get you very high on some concoction of drugs, and then lead you into a chamber full of hallucinogenic smoke where one of them would swing from a contraption pretending to be a ghost. Sounds pretty lame doesn't it? It was.

I digress. We will get across the lake using your coin and I will introduce you to Hades and Persephone sitting regally on their thrones. You will think he looks stern but not as dark as you might have expected. Just maybe a bit bored. And she will look both distant, like she doesn't really want to be there, and petrifying, when she turns to you and looks directly into your heart.

At that point I will take my leave of you for I have other places to be. You will be a little surprised because you thought it was a round trip. But I will point out that the ticket I gave you at the start said "Non-return".

Sorry.

YACHT ROCK

A. C. KOCH

t's easier to notice a bad pattern than a good one. For example, it only took Sam two occasions to realize that any time he played "Corcovado" while a girlfriend was in the room, she would end up getting decapitated in a freak car accident on the way home. Once was an accident; twice was a curse.

A subtler pattern, however, took much longer to rise to the level of his consciousness. He was in his mid-30s before he realized that every time a relationship ended—no matter who ended it—the song that was playing while they took their last looks at each other was Toto's "Africa." Blasting from a passing car, grooving on the mall's muzak, no matter how he heard it, once that song was over, he never saw that girlfriend again.

When he was dating Amy, he tried playing "Africa" for her, just to see what would happen. This was just after he'd noticed the pattern, and he was testing his theory. They hadn't been fighting or anything, it was only their fourth date and they were having a lovely romantic picnic on a summer afternoon. He strummed his ukulele and sang, "I hear the drums echoing tonight,..." and she leaned in, laughing.

Halfway through the first chorus, her phone trilled with an incoming text. She glanced at the message and her eyes went wide. She shot to her feet. "You bastard!" she screamed, and slapped him hard across the face. Then she spun and marched away across the grass.

Stunned, he went on strumming the chords until she faded from view on a pathway through the trees. The ukulele went silent, and he never saw her again.

For breakups, he had two powerful options. But if there was a pattern to how he could meet women and get them to like him, he hadn't figured it out yet. It seemed to be some combination of smiling and saying words and dressing reasonably well, but he hadn't narrowed it down to something as specific as a song.

After the whole Amy debacle, he started taking notes on all the times he went out looking for love. A couple of times he met nice women in bars, and hit it off, and once even made out with a waitress in the hallway going back to the restrooms where Metallica was audible from the kitchen ("Enter Sandman") while Jamiroquoi was grooving in the front part of the bar ("Canned Heat"). But nothing more came from that encounter, so the pattern eluded him.

It was during a perfectly ordinary trip to the supermarket that he met someone special. Their carts collided in the entryway as she was coming in and he was going out. The bag of apples in his cart spilled into hers. She wasn't really his type—more of an all-American yoga lady than the artsy, gothic types he usually went for—but she laughed as he showered her in apologies. She ended up carrying his apples out to his car with him, and handed him her business card after they'd chatted a few minutes. She added her cell number on the back, and flicked him the card with a grin. Pocketing it, he watched her walk into the supermarket. He gave her a few minutes to get lost in the aisles and then he marched back inside.

He wasn't going after her; he wanted a word with the manager.

"What was the song that was playing on the sound system about ten minutes ago?"

The manager stood behind the customer service desk and blinked. "The song?"

"It's a playlist, right? You have like a playlist running on the sound system, of corporate-approved shopping music. Right?"

It took a lot of wheedling but Sam finally got the manager to go into the back office and give him a run-down of all the songs that had played in the last twenty minutes. Sam noted the time and the song that was currently playing, then consulted his receipt for the rough time when he'd gone through the check-out. A little addition and subtraction narrowed it down to "Sailing," by Christopher Cross. Yacht Rock.

A confident smile flickered across his lips. He pulled his cell out and dialed in the number the woman had just given him.

"Hi—it's me, Sam, from the parking lot? I know it's only been a few minutes but I'm thinking I'd really love to see you again. What do you say we go grab a drink when you're done with your shopping?"

She hesitated and then laughed away from the phone. "Well," she said, and he could tell just by the sound of it that she was smiling.

Really, the story should end there. If it ended there, it would be a light-hearted bit of romance with a dash of magic, about how one man learns to take control of his romantic destiny, and learns a bit about life in the process.

It would be best to leave out the part about how he realized he could manipulate and monetize his bizarre gift, which—once he nailed down the pattern—never failed him. Best to skip the part about how he stalked a famous actress to play her the beginning of "Sailing" as she sat eating lunch with her agent in a downtown LA brasserie, how her eyes locked onto his as he strode through the tables with his ukulele, strumming and crooning. Six months later: his face and hers, pressed together in the flash bulbs, on the covers of paparazzi magazines across the world. Then everything falling to pieces when they were Christmas shopping in Barney's and "Africa" came on the speakers. In under a minute she was storming off, a red handprint throbbing on his cheek, camera flashes recording his stunned face. Then: a plunge into shame and despair. Best to skip over how he started lurking on the Dark Web to see who might be interested in hiring someone who could get a person decapitated.

It turns out a lot of people are in the market for that.

He took a job that involved going to a Washington D.C. cocktail party and bumping into a woman who was a high-profile lobbyist for an environmental group. His ukulele looked ridiculous with his tuxedo, but a chorus of "Sailing" later and she was sparkling eyes at him and running her fingernail up his arm. Later, after hotel sex, he sat on the love seat strumming. He alternated between the opening chords of "Africa" and "Corcovado." One would get her to leave, unharmed, while the other would result in her losing her head. The first option was worth nothing, but the second was worth a million.

"I had a nice time," she said as she came out of the bathroom steaming, wrapping a towel around her body.

He smiled, and started strumming. She swayed as he sang along, "Quiet nights of quiet stars..."

flash fiction

RUNNER UP

RALPH PENNEL

illy patted the mound of dirt with the back of the shovel then wiped his brow with his sleeve. It was done. He grabbed his pick and shovel and headed to his car through the thick covering of trees. He blamed the dog for this. A chocolate lab. 6 months old and still so much puppy. It was impossible to get her to sit still. ZuZu. As in ZuZu's petals from the movie It's a Wonderful Life, the one where George Bailey dives into the water to save his guardian angel after his guardian angel jumps in the icy water to save him. Then he gets a chance to see how his life affected the lives of those around him for the better. Billy wanted to see himself as George, but really, he was more like Ernie the cab driver. A minor character. Not integral to the plot. Charming in his own way, but ultimately dispensable. It was the reason he asked her if he could "shoot her dog for the competition." This longing. It seemed like a sign. Like this was the chance to change his life's path.

"Excuse me?" she said.

"You know, take her picture," he said. "I'm a photographer. Pet photographer." He showed her his Pet Photographer's guild card. She scrutinized it carefully, turning it over a few times before handing it back. It was a strange thing to ask on a second date he knew, but he was so struck by the origins of the name that it seemed like Kismet. And ZuZu was gorgeous. Full bred. Luxurious floppy ears. Golden eyes. Healthy coat. It's the only reason he asked the girl out in the first place. For the dog. But he wasn't the only one who did this. Ted, the unassuming, scrawny guy with those glasses that turn to shades in the sun, who managed the Rite Aid at the end of his block, and the reigning Middlesex County Pet Photographer champ, invented the move. He was so smooth. He'd have a girl's permission to shoot her pet before the first date was even set. He could spot a pure bred at half a mile. He'd be across the street and through two cross walks against the red just catch up with her before you even knew what it was he was after.

Billy blamed the dog, but he knew that wasn't right. He had been distracted. The girl, ZuZu's owner, was pretty. Really pretty. At one point he found himself plotting out their third date. He caught himself daydreaming about holding her hand in a movie or sharing an ice cream on the esplanade. He even caught himself imagining just how he'd propose to her. He'd think about her at work, while sorting the mail, which had gotten him in trouble with his manager, who insisted he "get his head out of his ass before he put it in there for him." Which didn't particularly make sense but was still effective for helping him regain his focus, which was on winning this year's Middlesex County Pet Photography shoot off. The problem was, he let her help. First rule of Pet Photography is you never let the owner help you "stay" the pet. Everyone knows this. It only takes one blurred shot, or one dog who won't sit up, or who won't stop wagging its tongue to get it out of your system though. There is too much at stake.

It was over dessert when he asked. It all happened in slow motion. He heard himself asking as if he had no control of his own voice and before he knew it she had said yes. He couldn't take it back. He tried to convince himself it would be okay. She's good with the dog, he said. She can handle the pressure. And, really, what happened could have happened to anyone. But they had just gotten ZuZu steady after nearly 20 minutes of working with her when the girl coughed. It was dry in the building where the competition was being held, and when she coughed she raised her hand to her mouth politely, which distracted ZuZu the exact moment Billy took the shot. ZuZu had only flinched a little, but it was enough. The red ribbon hanging by his photo in the finalist's gallery, watching Ted take home yet another trophy and the $10,000 cash prize didn't compare to the betrayal he felt, though, and couldn't return the ring he'd bought on sale that he'd plotted to give to her while standing on the winner's stand, trophy in one hand, her ring bejeweled hand in the other. When he got back to his car, he glanced at the backseat where ZuZu had been lying peacefully moments before. He paused briefly before tossing the shovel and pick into the trunk. He knew he couldn't keep her. But he needed some sort of prize. Something that felt like this was a wonderful life.

When I Die Play the Sounds of Thelonious Monk and Miles Davis at My Funeral

J. B. STONE

As I lay, six feet under. As
maggots feast on my remains,
turn my funeral into a more
traditional wake, Pagan,
Earthy in death's delight. Save
my loved ones the thousands
in funeral home expenses, save
them the generic semantics,
for another rendition of
Amazing Grace, or a prayer
from holy men I never knew
and will never know. Let the
soundtrack of this mourning
be a solace sound of haunting
joy. Let the piles of vinyl you
leave beside my tombstone,
be a surrogate for a rose bouquet.
Let the scores be composed for
the dawn of Autumn Leaves and
nightlife moments revolving
'Round Midnight. Let the aura
of Blue in Green cover your
grief in Milestones for a
tomorrow worth carrying

Tsadde is Not the Star in the Thoth Tarot Deck

VICTORIA NORDLUND

In my spread
you and the Emperor are now side by side.
I imagine that you would not be happy
with this present arrangement.

Aleister Crowley, in contact
with an extra dimensional entity, Aiwaz,
discovered that you were not
in your proper place, that
all these old letters were not aright
and decided, just like that,
to switch the Emperor card with you.

Tsadde
Great Mother bare
before me.
Resolver of the Tower
Gifter of the Spirit
Woman structualizing energy
in dual flow.
Woman putting the fish hook
deep within herself
to reveal the unseen hiding
place where real knowledge lies.
Woman who has Venus
and seven Chakras shining for you,
who has Ibis as your audience
as all the water you pour forth
circles back to the source—

should really know your fucking place.

You were never meant to represent Strength.

See, the Emperor was always better suited:
sitting on a ram-skulled stone throne
Bearded/armored/crowned/robed
in red and orange.
Clutching his orb and Ankh,
barren mountain behind him.
He thinks he is the shit.

Crowley was convinced
he held the world,
thought you looked fine
balancing those pitchers.
Changed your role,
gave you Justice instead.

This is bullshit, I say,
Stand up from the pools
that flow at your feet
Put your hook through eyes
that will not meet yours
and tell him he has never lead you.

But there you are—
still together
in my present and future
unable to alter your position.

And I listen dutifully to the interpretation
of my final outcome—
giving the reader way too much power,
waiting to hear a revelation,
waiting for someone to change me too.

HIGH PRIESTESS

VICTORIA NORDLUND

I admit, I totally wanted the Magician
somewhere in this relationship spread
even though he's just a try-hard card who
waves his wand and
craves an audience
to applaud his slick sleights of hand,
to kiss his sword of intellect.
Thinks he's hot stuff with his lemniscate
setting the universe on fire.
But he never appears for me.

I get you.
You are my outcome position.
I tell myself you are a
pretty cool, self-sufficient witch
who would prefer to keep her magic
on the down-low.

You don't really need anyone, do you?

Veiled one in blue robe
with Hathor's headdress,
with resting bitch face,
and no apologies,
with hands rooted to arcane scrolls
that hold all the answers.
You withdraw willingly
with the moon and the waters
of the sky at your feet.
You yield,
and the world just comes to you
asking for its future.
You sit in front

of this pomegranate tapestry
that decorates the blank wall
I always thought was a path.

Perched between darkness and light
by the pillars of Solomon's temple:
Boaz and Jachin
Black and White
Negation and Beginning.
You are not a gate
or a portal
or a bridge
to pass through,
or to walk across.
You are the middle pillar,
the tree,
the stillness.

I fold you into the others and
reshuffle my deck.
I am the Fool
grasping that little white rose,
asking the same question,
seeking my course of action,
about to step off a cliff.

THE HANGED MAN

VICTORIA NORDLUND

Suspended by my own will,
right foot bound,
left foot free,
I tell myself it's OK
because there is no noose
around my neck.
I am here
in this grayness
because I chose
to be a martyr
in this nothing—
upside down
in this tree
that seems to be living.
I am already hanged.
Done hanging on—

There is victory in this surrender.
So much power in yielding
to the universe.
So much time now
since I stopped moving forward.
Any way you turn the card
I will still be in this position—
rooted to the underworld,
or
shouldering the heavens—
See, it really doesn't matter.
I left myself
here holding my own hands
behind my back,
wearing my blue coat, red tights,
and serene smile

I will never take off,
convincing myself
I am plenty
comfortable in the warmth
of my own halo.

UNKNOWN KIN(D)

ANNE RUNDLE

1.

Your bones hadn't yet chosen a gender
so I can name you Daisy or Stella or Ralph.
If you'd survived I'd have
another box or circle (to type letters inside)
on our family tree instead of this question mark.
Disposed of instead of buried,
a miscarriage leaves only questions
in its wake.

2.

Family secrets kept in a cardboard box:
three near-empty bottles of whiskey.
Such a forked path gives two choices:
a swig pours heat down one's throat
or trickles down the sink
followed by admitting imperfection
accept the things… courage to change… wisdom
that this addiction feels necessary, like breathing air.
Stride one day at a time
to detox and sobriety and meetings,
or walk the other way
with a liver hardening
into a stiff grey
scare tactic on Dr. Oz.

3.

Actually, these weren't secrets.
Everyone knew how it played out.
One man died young in my life,

a candle flicker during a blackout,
and the other lived to see
my older brother's high school graduation.

4.

I come to sit in the chapel
while an organist practices her scales,
teaches a piano lesson, & I hum wordless songs
full of chords and pedals and echoes.
You call from the beyond.
Here, I let my ghosts find me.
It's my routine. The days
may feel as if I'm at a factory assembling pens,
as if I don't have to think, only follow
the same steps for years on end.
Here I can hear my thoughts in the music,
look outside, see traffic lights change yellow
into red and ambulance sirens screeching.

5.

The family ghosts I miss the most
are absent, long established
in heaven and no longer in *It's a Wonderful Life*
transitions. They are angels who guard me,
with a hands-off role.
I see eyes that twinkle,
dimpled smiles & a cackle that
sounds like a witch, but is simply
her sound of bliss.

6.

The ghosts stay on the sidelines, a
cheerleading squad I can feel
by the color of the skies.
Sunrise, sunset and
sunbeams peeking out after a storm

are when they paint
small messages from the other side.
When the snow falls, I see
their gift in the differences of
snow in one single day: sleet,
hail, wet snow, slow fluffy snow,
and I am reminded Inuits
have multiple words for snow.

7.

A man on the radio
states cemetery comes from
the Latin for temporary resting
place, as dormitory means a
place we sleep. When I see tombstones,
I consider if the ending dates were removed,
if these boxes weren't decomposing
underground, or in my family's
case, boxes of ashes buried
under grass left damp by snow
shaded by an oak tree, and
dandelions always reappearing near
the edges of their gravestones.

8.

If those years etched in stone
could be uncarved
these relatives could still
answer my phone calls.
Now, they only answer
telepathically and only
vanish when I need them
most, knowing I must walk
alone, knowing I miss their syrup and
pancakes, letters in the mailbox and replenishing
all the backyard's birdhouses to sit in wait.

9.

Two cardinals always visit my
parents' yard, and a host
of robins sing in my yard.
The snow melts, and
their gravestones warm under the sun.

NANTUCKET SLOUGH

JULIE ALLYN JOHNSON

Airborne insects buzz and whine,
cicadas drone on, an infinite loop.
Shimmery wings
    skim the fetid stench,
    the muddy ooze
    of this desolate marsh.
Papery appendages soar
    amid a hushed spectacle of sound.
Cattails burst on gusts of wind,
    nocturnal beings creep into the night.

Onlookers,
mindless of the pending menace,
flit and skitter and alight in the gathering dusk.

White noise, boggy waters.

Twin beams pierce the twilight:
    1961 Lincoln Continental
    Tahitian Turquoise
    rusted fender
    broken antennae.
Sweet crunch of rubber striking gravel,
tires rolling to an ominous halt.
Driver's door opens, then — thunk — slams shut.

Footsteps
    slow and deliberate
    taunting.

Nursing the stub of a Camel Light,
the driver squints his eyes
and inhales the smoke of his delayed longing.

He pauses then pops the trunk
peers inside
tossing his cigarette.

Mockingly tender, he reaches for her.
A struggle ensues but quickly ends
        for one is bound
            the other is free.

Unshackling her,
he speaks in low measured tones
then utters a
            single
            paralyzing
            command:
            Run.

Eyes wide, so wide:
the match has been struck,
her fate determined.

He nudges her forward.
She stumbles,
            falls to the ground,
            arms outstretched,
            eyes grasping at the black veil before her.
Slowly she rises.

The man waits, relishing her fear.
Hesitant at first,
            she steps forward
            then does as she's been told.

The game begins.

And in the inky blackness
an upright creature snarls
and roars his bloody mouth.

There's a Secret Out There, When No One Is Watching

VALIN PAIGE

somewhere out in the desert
is a body – murdered & forgotten

        buried deep in the yellows &
        oranges of New Mexico or Arizona

waiting to be dug up hastily
with a notched shovel that will

        scrape against its dry ribs
        & gouge out bits of skull

someone will wipe sweat
from their brow & take a quick

        drink of water from a dusty
        bottle before continuing this

work, eventually pulling teeth
& ribs & good hip tips from

        the dry earth – will then smile
        see something familiar in all

those bones – something worth
being drawn to in the early morning

        hours with a knife or crowbar
        & a filthy kind of hunger

there is something magic being
nowhere in the desert with a shovel

        something magic about being old
        knowing there is a living with terrible

secrets & then this person smiles
rummaging in these memories

        & a dead thing that knows, but
        perhaps the bones heard of revenge

from the earth, spent years planning
for something good like this

                the shoveler watches
                the bones begin to shift, thinks it is the wind

at first – then the bones move
faster, turn their sharp bits on

                a familiar face, begin to cut in & out
                over & over again until there again is

quiet & the yellows & oranges
begin to take everything back down into

                the dancing, ecstatic dust

LUST #7

DECEMBER LACE

They keep me in neon basement dungeons
Where red lights flash on/off in the stairway
The chains and leather that breed me come in droves

Salt stained bodies writhing on grime-soaked sheets
Skin sticking together like glue
The dirt seeping in far deeper than the fabric

I tell them I bring them gifts
I tell them I bring them promise
The teeth gnawing on each other, enamel breaking

Thrashing for water, fighting for air
They want me as though I were religion
The escape, sealed off forever by doors built decades ago

Dark faces seething through locked jaws
Twisted ecstasies and thrusting pelvises
The ways I won't wake them, the ways I let them stay

poetry

SECRET LIFE

ROBIN WRIGHT

Two weeks after my friend's death, her husband calls, wants to get together and talk about her secret life. I know what he's doing. He's searching through belongings, studying pictures of her with large glasses, big hair, and a young son tethered to her neck. He's reading letters from her life-long pen-pal, wondering what words are painted on the other side of the canvas. He wants to know the her before their five years together, wants me to share twenty-five years of tender gifts unwrapped in my brain. I can't think of anything secret. He already knows about the stripper I hired for her thirty-fifth birthday. *Best birthday ever*, she always said. A night of steak, wine, a muscular man gyrating to a boom box and the squeals of several women. Maybe it's realization that the shape of new memories has dissolved into sand or that the power of addition, five years plus another twenty-five, equals a life, that's made him call. My secret: I want spring to bring more than sweet-smelling blossoms to my tulip tree, and deep-red berries to the holly. I want my friend to jump up, leave her cancer in damp dirt, wave her arms, and shout.

SEPARATION ANXIETY

NICOLE RIVERA

The girl liked her nose, its crust-crowded rims
and sultry dripping.
She liked to be awake all night, compelled, eyes skipping
across the chipped ceiling's constellation
of cocaine. She liked to snort alone
in her dim room the tea-tint color
of library book paper.
She liked the door locked so the ghost couldn't enter. The ghost
taunted itself, tried to follow and ask if she'd like
some oatmeal for breakfast. The girl refused, deafened by the off-
white lull of the apartment hallway.
Instead, she liked scratching the powder off the bureau
with her metrocard, unrolling the dollar bill, licking the leftovers
off the edges, her throat burning on stale sour gulps.
She liked not eating, not getting hungry, her stomach
flat and coiling while her bones crippled from winter
sickness, but she liked that too.
She liked her baggy tights, no pockets for tip money,
more to blow on blow to blacken her
cushioned eyes with small bags of sugar dusted rocks.
But then she saw
her mother in the mirror, the ghost she thought
she locked out, their wasted faces overlapped, her mother's
flickerlight whispers falling short of conversation, again,
just as it was before she left. The girl's sleepless face
stirred in a brown blur with her matted hair,
her eyeliner swiped with crying, she echoed in withdrawal. Her cold comforter ruffled
and absorbed her, and still, nobody came home.

WALKING ON MIRRORS

NICOLE RIVERA

I.

Your mother left
flowers on the table, drove off
in a u-haul. What old affection
dies--she didn't miss
you. There is white
noise between this side
and that. One building, one
house, one travel.

II.

Your letters never read
dear mother, are you enjoying
the great distance? The words
were petals of a fake rose, I miss you,
conditional, frail. Who was better
at telling a lie? Your mirror, your mother,
the table's leftovers.

III.

The thorned stem cripples
across the street, one last reach
for petals. The frosted
ground spreads like cracked
ice, your hands ash numb. You look
down, think about the incisions,
how do roots grow
through tiny slithers
of space, erase blankness in the ground?

IV.

What a great distance
for you to travel, no mom, no hands
to hold or help you
cross. Look both ways! Don't trip
and fall. There is nothing beautiful
about a mind of winter, the deserted,
twisted ground, your resemblance to her.

HOSPICE

NICOLE RIVERA

October's dry breeze, its crusted soil
greybrown, clustered in clumps welcomed my grandmother's
grave, spirit engrained in a wall
made of granite, stamped with gold lettering
boxed and neighbored to strangers, young
and spoiled by frequent lilies.
Last year she lied awake
in a different box, silenced white, fuzzy.
Her eyes slightly rolled back,
her lips ashy and foamed, forced to entertain
a slow tempo of air, ballad of her sleep.
It's a lie when they say
the bodies can hear, unconscious
and charging on an outlet.
After sitting there for hours I asked her
for permission, anyway,
to step out for something to eat.
I didn't think, *how long is she willing
to wait?*
October apparent and in my hands,
the silver slash of wind against
my unprotected body,
and her last breath, cotton-muffled
unheard, unwarranted. The stiffening
sheets lingered for nine hours after,
the buffyellow desert stain stretched
across her skin and still,
I watched.

ONE LESS LIKE

BEN TARI

Steve stared at the image. It had come through as he was catching up on some emails and it had distracted him enough. His pizza was cold and the rest of the house quiet. Now he zoned in.

'Us in the Royal National Park. So pretty!'

There was Helen in all her glory; big grin, tight T and jeans. Next to her the kids, both predictably also smiling. Her husband looked almost rugged in the photo even though he spent most his life in front of a computer. He had a Clark Kent cowlick. In the background a black lake and a forest of dark Eucalypts disappearing into a cave.

He imagined them lying on the dank cave floor. Wet rocks behind their scuffed faces. Short, sharp breaths. Air thick with sweat and bile. His mouth watching them try to break their bonds.

The photograph irked Steve. It was a lie. It was manufactured and ignored the shitty, boring everyday stuff. It made Steve feel like a crappy father. His kids rarely asked for him anymore. His wife had stopped pretending she wanted him. Guilt followed him everywhere. It hovered around the edges and rapped on his consciousness asking questions he tried to avoid.

The cave was gone, replaced by a kitchen. The family now lay huddled tight in a corner, against the cupboards. Floor slippery with fear. He looked the worst. He was avoiding eye contact and trying to make himself smaller. A dark patch grew on his chinos. The urine thinned the blood spreading across the checkered lino. He sometimes squawked quietly like a half-dead bird.

The family in the picture was showing off. You could hear them.

'Look at us in this totally amazing forest! We are so at one with nature! Let's share it with everyone so they'll know how loving and generous and super-duper our family is!'

Steve hated them.

Now his attention turned to Helen. Her blouse was torn. She was attempting to protect her off-spring by placing herself between her kids and him. She was ready to fight. To protect her young. Her face set in defiance. He lurched at her, the knife clumsy in his hands.

What did he really have in common with them anyway? Steve couldn't remember when he'd last felt close to them. He'd certainly never felt welcomed by them. They were more acquaintances than anything. His finger hovered as he took one final look at the post.

Outside, an early morning garbage truck gurgled down the road.

He brushed the cowlick off his forehead, clicked 'unfriend' and left the room.

flash fiction

BAIT

ZURI MCWHORTER

1 t was my fault. Mama always said, "Don't leave the baby alone. Night time is pretty to look at, but don't you go out and leave that baby alone." I ain't know why I always had to watch after her, but when Mama made a rule, I followed it.

There was a party in town for the Mayor's birthday. Big Sir took Mama with him cuz she's so pretty and he likes to show her off. She could pass for one of them Creole ladies if she made her lips red and combed out her fluffs. I couldn't go to parties cuz I was too little and "too nappy". I ain't wanna go no way cuz it was a pretty night and I wanted to go look at the moon dance with the swamp.

I know I wasn't sposed to leave the baby. But the baby was fine. She was sleepin' so good cuz the breeze was blowin' the chimes against the hangin' tree, makin' a nice noise to sleep to. She was gon' be fine.

I kissed her sweaty forehead and snuck out of the shack. It was easy that night cuz all the white people was gone and all the niggas was sleep.

When I got outside, I heard the bugs screamin' and followed em down to the water. Then I heard some screamin' of another kind. They were little screams, whimpers like a puppy. It wasn't no words, just scared yelps bouncin' through the bayou. I thought an animal was hurt or some-thin', so I went to see what's the matter.

> The rope man held up a brown jug of liquor and took a big gulp. Then, outta nowhere, a giant gator came and snapped down on the rope.

Down this muddy hill, near the river, I saw a rusty cage. The little screams was coming from it. Then I saw a white man, and some rope. Another white man with a torch. Another white man with a gun.

I got closer and hid behind a willow tree, being quiet as I could. It ain't so bad bein' dark skinned when it's night time cuz people don't see you good. Then I saw what was inside the screamin' cage. It was full of nigga babies, naked and cryin'. There was a bucket of pig fat next to it. The white man grabbed a baby girl out of the cage, greased her up, and tied the rope 'round her neck, real tight. The moonlight made her shiny skin glow. She screamed loud as she could.

The white man threw her into the water and she tried to swim before she got too tired and drowned. I was on the other side of the tree by now to see what they was fishin' for. The rope man just stood there, spittin' snuff and makin' talk with the other white men.

"Dat party prolly a lot mo' fun den catchin' gatas."

"Yeah, but dis' gon be 'nuff tuh hol' us ova til de next one." I think that was the torch man.

The rope man held up a brown jug of liquor and took a big gulp. Then, outta nowhere, a giant gator came and snapped down on the rope. Hard.

"Shit!" the rope man yelled. The gun man took a shot straight into the gators head. Like a habit.

The water stilled and the gator waded until the rope man went in, opened its dead jaws, and took what was left of the baby girl out. He threw her out into the swamp.

I couldn't hear what they was sayin' after that. I ain't realize that I was screamin' now, too. I ran as fast as I could toward the shack. They didn't chase after me, though. I turned and saw they was still just standin' there, doin' they business. I started screamin' again, but nothing was comin' out. They ain't hear me the first time, neither.

I ran to check on the baby. But she was gone. They took her while I was gone! I ran back out-side and couldn't see nothin' cuz my eyes was burning with scared sweat. I ain't wanna go back down to the swamp so I just fell on the ground and cried. Then a sweet, whisper startled me.

"Chile, what you doin' out her makin' all that fuss for?"

It was Mama! She was holding the baby, still sweaty and sleepin'. I got up and held onto my Mama.

"I went to the swamp! You told me not to! I saw what they do to the babies."

"Hush girl!" We went back into the shack and Mama sat me down on her lap, with the baby in her arms.

"Miss May caught you runnin' down, so she came and took the baby to her shack." Mama was calm, but still scary to me. I wiped my eyes and tried to catch my breath.

"I'm sorry Mama."

"What I tell you? Don't leave that baby alone. Now you know why, dontcha?"

short story

STONES

CRAIG ANDERSON

1 read once that in the movie Psycho, Hitchcock used chocolate syrup for blood. Mingled with the shower water, it had a similar consistency as it ran down the tiles and swirled around the drain. The real stuff, trickling across the sand and into the water of Manitou Lake, looks nothing like that. I lift my foot and see the small stone beneath, it's sharp edge stained red. The cut on my big toe is too small to see, except for the drops of blood that still cling to it.

The lake is calm today, a blue-green portal reflecting the surrounding walls of birch and pine. This patch of sand is one of the only openings in the treeline around the lake. There used to be a dock here, really just a couple of wooden pallets tied together, but that floated away years ago. There used to be a cottage too. My grandfather built it for my grandma as a wedding gift. At least that was the story she always told. All that's left now is the mile-long dirt driveway, somehow still holding its own against the encroaching forest.

It's the driveway that has me worried. I practically grew up here. I've traveled the dirt road through the trees a hundred times. I know which sections of overgrowth hide potholes, and where the gravel has been washed away by rain. I could drive the entire mile with my eyes closed. I can't say the same for him.

Hayden has never been here.

We talked about coming. During those first few weeks when we still lived in one another's orbit, and each of us was hungry for any chance to learn something new about the other. Or later, when he was fucking around, and a picnic at the lake seemed like a good way to prove that he was "making an effort." During our three years together, I came to the lake plenty of times, but today will be Hayden's first. That is, if he was being honest about wanting to see me. And, if he didn't find something better to do on a Sunday afternoon. And, if his car makes it down the driveway.

Sunlight hits the surface of the lake, highlighting the variations in color. Here, closer to shore, the clear water takes on the greenish brown of the lake floor. About fifty yards out, at the point of the drop off into deeper water, the color takes an abrupt shift to dark blue. As a kid, I spent countless summer hours daring myself to wade closer and closer to the green-blue border.

"Not too far."

My grandmother stood a few yards behind me, near the makeshift dock, pulling a garden rake across the lake floor. She wore her purple swimsuit, with the ruffly faux skirt that extended down past her thighs (an "old lady bather," my mother use to call it). Stray wisps of gray poked out from beneath her daytime wig of soft brown curls. She grumbled as she raked, muttering about the number of stones and how she should have worn her sandals. Small piles of stones sat behind her at the water's edge.

"That's far enough," she said.

I stood halfway between her and the dropoff, the waterline hovering just below my five year-old chest. She set the rake on the dock and gestured for me. I waded back toward shore, taking a brief detour to watch a young water snake swim past, its smooth, speckled body zigzagging across the surface.

When I reached my grandmother, I plopped down on the dock and let my feet dangle in the water. She sat next me, the pallet creaking beneath her. She was winded from raking, so we sat in silence for a moment, my grandma's breathing mixing with the lapping of the water against the wood. When I turned toward her, she was staring out over the lake.

"Gramma?" I said, following her gaze toward the center of the lake. "Do you miss Grandpa?" She let out a long breath, and nodded.

"He was a good man," she said, still looking at the water. "I wish you could have known him. He found this lake, and build the cottage just for--"

"I know," I said. "You told me that already."

"Of course," she said. Her voice lowered to a breathy whisper. "When I think about what he sacrificed for our family." She wiped a bony hand across her cheek, and glanced down at me. I had already moved on from this moment of reflection, and was swirling my foot in the water to attract a school of minnows. She looked back out to the lake. "He was such a strong swimmer."

One of the tiny fish nibbled at my big toe and I squealed.

"Come on," My grandmother said, standing. "We'd better head in before we're both too waterlogged to move."

I giggled, and she took my hand and led me onto the sand, where we practiced making shapes with the stones.

I am thinking about checking my phone, which is stuffed into my shoe a few feet from the water's edge, when I hear Hayden's car.

"You know," he says. His dark hair is shorter now, and somehow it makes his eyes seem bluer. "If you're gonna insist on meeting out in BFE, the least you can do is answer my texts. I passed the drive three times."

"Sorry."

> She glanced down at me and looked back out to the lake. "He was such a strong swimmer."

I realize I'm looking at him in that way that I told myself I wouldn't. That way that says he looks better than I expected. That way that says I miss looking at him.

"I mean," Hayden says, looking up at the trees."We usually just meet at a bar or something for this kind of thing, instead of driving into the wilderness."

"This kind of thing?" I say. "I didn't tell you why I wanted to see you."

I know what he means. I usually make it about three or four months without seeing him before one of us, usually me, calls the other and suggests we talk. And he's right, it doesn't usually involve a two-hour drive from the city. It usually involves us spending the night together. Sometimes, several nights. Last time, it was almost a month.

"I'm sorry," he says, putting his palms up in a gesture of surrender. "He's wearing a white t-shirt with a deep enough v-neck to show that he's stepped up his chest workouts. "What I meant to say," he says. "Is that it's good to see you."

He's not a hugger. So, when he steps in and puts his arms around me, it catches me off guard. At least, until his hand lands on my ass. He leans in until his lips are brushing against my ear. "You look good, Kev," he says. "You look real good."

"You too," I say. I know that if I turn my head just a little, he'll kiss me. That's what I should do. It would be the smart thing. But, I don't like how warm his arms feel, how comfortable. Instead, I take a step back from him and look out toward the water.

"So this is the lake you were always talking about," Hayden says.

"This is it," I say. "Only took me four years to get you here."

He fakes a chuckle. From somewhere across the water, a loon cries.

"Why am I here, Kevin?" he says.

"I wanted to see you." It's not the answer I planned, but when I practiced what I would say, Hayden wasn't standing in front of me with his blue eyes and his deep v.

"But why all the way out here?"

"You know how special this place is to me. I thought maybe if you were willing to drive out here—"

"Wait, this was some kind of test?" he says.

I'm blowing this.

"It's not like that," I say. "It's such a warm day. I thought we could take a swim. You still owe me a do-over after all." Years ago, on our second date, Hayden took me to a pool party. When I told him I had spent a semester on my high school swim team, he challenged me to a race across the pool and back. It's not that he was faster than me, just more motivated to win.

"Are you serious? You want to swim?" he asks.

I nod, and pull my shirt off. Hayden looks at me, then the water, then back at me. He smiles.

"So," he says, already lifting the t-shirt over his head. "If I beat you across, is the prize the same as last time?"

I step closer to him, put my hand on his chest, slide it down the smooth ridges of his stomach and under the waistband of jeans. He's half hard, but I don't flatter myself. Hayden has always lived in a constant state of readiness. He puts his hand on my wrist, coaxing me further beneath his jeans.

"How about we skip the swim race and go straight to the victory celebration?" he says.

I pull my hand out, and slide down my shorts.

"You have to beat me first," I say.

In a few seconds, our clothes are in a pile and we're stepping over the stones on the sand and into the water. It's warm, and I can feel a gentle undercurrent swirling over my ankles. Hayden doesn't take time to appreciate any of this. He's focused on winning, already bounding through the shallows.

"It's no fun if you let me win," he calls back to me. I break into an awkward trot.

When the water reaches his waist, he looks back at me, and then dives forward with his arms stretched out in front of his head. I slog through the thigh-high water, but he's already passing the point where the water goes dark. His body lunges forward through the blue, the pale globes of his ass breaking through the surface like the hump of a dolphin.

I stop a few feet from the drop off and watch him. He's in better shape than when we were together. Such a strong swimmer. For a second I consider yelling to him, calling him back.

Then I see it.

There's a rise in the dark water, several yards to the east, a sort of swell like a bubble rising to the surface. Then another, closer to Hayden. I realize that I'm back-stepping toward the shore, eyes still fixed forward. The water starts to swell a third time, and then it happens fast. So fast, I'm not exactly sure what I'm seeing. Not exactly. There's a glint of sunlight just above the waterline near Hayden, and then the lake seems to open up in front of him. The dark shape that launches up through the surface is almost indistinguishable from the color of the water, except when the sunlight hits a blue-gray scale. It is wider in the back and tapers into a pointed snout, but I can't tell that for sure because it is stretching open, growing into a toothy maw, almost large enough to engulf the naked swimmer. Hayden tries to scream, but only has time for a gurgled croak as the teeth come down on him. There is a spray of scarlet in the air as the thing drags him under. When the blood hits the water it darkens, floating on the surface like a cloud of ink, or chocolate syrup.

I stare at the place where Hayden had been for a few more seconds, before turning and making my way back to the shore. I walk out of the water and onto the sand, stepping over the place where the stones are arranged in the ancient summoning symbols. 🌑

short story

ROTTING FRUIT

RACHEL HEHL

*Segments in italics taken from Cecilia Woloch's poem 'Hades'

here we go when he closes my eyes…

WPollen coats her feet like party glitter on her Abduction Day. She'd been kicking at the budding spellflowers, her mother's newest creation, turning up the earth, squishing dirt between her toes.

She thinks that's what attracted him. The slaughter of the flowers, her spiteful laugh as she'd trampled on what spring had so painstakingly coaxed into bloom. Turns out you can catch flies with more than honey. Her tantrum drew the eye of a monster.

Tall and distorted with shadow, a hooded figure rises from an unseen pit and grasps her by the arm. She can't help screaming when its fingers, soot-blackened and conjoined by a membranous web of adipocere, slide over her wrist, leaving a smear of fluid almost like the glistening trail of a mollusc. For a second, she believes in those tired mortal nightmare tales of zombies and mummies, of putrefied corpses rising from graveyard soil to feast on ripe flesh. She's heard it all before – there are no such monsters, not in Olympus – but for a second, she believes.

And then it mutters a curse and her knees give way, and the beast scoops her into its arms as though she is weightless. Her shift rides up her thighs obscenely, and she has time to blush at the indecency before that pit is gaping before them, a sightless abyss, and she wraps her arms around her captor's neck and clings on for dear life.

And together, they plunge into the world below.

Some blue darkness, further than hell…

It seems to her that strange galaxies swirl there, in the pinpricks of cold light in the blackness – she feels the pull of gravity lifting the hairs on her arms and head, floating fiery strands about her face. Or maybe what she feels is the absence of gravity, of matter unanchored, as her abductor wades through the dark, radiant shadows rippling in its wake.

Eventually, once her eyes have adjusted to the dark, she notices that the light is bouncing off water – creating the shimmering, cosmic effect she'd thought she'd seen. The beast carrying her is up to its knees, the hem of its cloak trailing like a prince's coronation robe in the muck. She peers down, trying to glimpse their shared reflection in the mirrored surface, but the beast snarls and grips the back of her head with one hand, shoving her face roughly into its shoulder. Persephone lets out a muffled cry, her mouth crushed against the fabric of its cloak, teeth pressed painfully against her lips. She expects the cloak to stink, imbued with the filth of rot and centuries, but it just smells faintly bitter, like citrus.

There's a brief splash as her kidnapper enters the shallows, then steps out of the water entirely, onto a more well-lit section of rock. An uneven shelf leads up to a staircase, cut into the feldspar and impregnated with seams of quartz, and Persephone stifles her gasp against the creature's shoulder as they climb, the crystals scintillating underfoot, a sea of stars.

There are no bodies here – we dream shapeless dreams…

They reach the top of the staircase, the maiden and the monster, with her arms still circling its throat like pearls. Her captor hesitates, and she chooses that moment to squirm and writhe, trying to break its grip. Her mouth is still pressed against its cloak - silencing her - and, instinctively, she peels her lips back to her gums and bites. Her teeth sink through fabric and flesh, and her captor grunts with pain, their vengeful fingers knotting themselves into her hair and yanking mercilessly. Her head rocks back on her spine, a frisson of golden sparks bursting before her eyes, and she kicks reflexively, one of her knees connecting with the monster's chin with a crack, the hood falling back from its skull to reveal the terror underneath-

And she spits in the monster's face. A glob of sticky, blood-tinged spittle lands on its cheek, slipping over skin the colour and temperature of metal.

For a moment, they stare at each other in disbelief. Then its lips crinkle with disgust and its arms fall away entirely, letting her slide clumsily to the floor. The creature wipes its cheek with the sleeve of its cloak, grimacing as Persephone watches, at once repulsed and spellbound by the sight of it.

Silver-dusted skin stretches over cheekbones as delicate and pronounced as those of a seraph in bas-relief, but the black veins - spidering up the sides of its face to form lightning forks around its eye sockets - are like cracks in porcelain, ugly and horribly apparent. Its black-lipped mouth curls back over teeth that are nothing more than serrated points, inset in dark gums. Its eyes are dark too, and as Persephone stares, they swivel to meet her gaze – she sees that they are a livid violet, the shade of the belladonna plants that grow in mother's nightgarden, bearing bloated, poisonous berries. Above those eyes sits a crown shaped out of bleached bone, milk-white and twisted – segments of the bone have crystallized into geodes, winking with baby amethyst crystals.

Beautiful, but deadly, she thinks, and then the monster is speaking to her, in a cracked, guttural voice that sounds like it hasn't been put to use in aeons.

'Who are you, brat, and why have you summoned me?'

She looks up at the beast defiantly, and her voice is quavering a touch when she replies, but she imbues her words with enough scorn it hardly matters. 'Who am I? Who are you?! I would think it is only politeness to let the hostage ask first.' She lifts her chin, expecting its answering wrath.

It doesn't come.

A constant, cloudless storm…

Hades looks down at this gremlin, this prickly little cactus of a woman in her grimy shift dress, with her orange hair like spreading wildfire and courage too great for her size. He's half infuriated, half amused, studying her chubby little face with its smattering of sun-bites and its contemptuous expression. Despite the dirtiness of her clothes, her skin underneath is clean, so pale between freckles it has a nacreous sheen, like the skin of a freshwater pearl. Her eyes burn into his - unwavering, a bottomless brown, the rich colour of the earth she'd torn up and thus summoned him.

Do you truly not know? he thinks with incredulity. After all, they've just crossed the river Styx - the stains from its putrid water are all over her dress. This girl is ignorant, he decides, but he'll grant her one answer.

'I am the king of the underworld,' he says with a sneer. 'And you are in hell. Do you still claim not to know me?'

He waits for the horror to dawn over her face, for those brown eyes to swim with tears, for him to beg her to return her to the surface. The way they all beseech him, those lost souls, both mortal and divine, on their knees at the foot of his throne.

But he is not on his throne, and the girl doesn't beg. Her eyes glint, a subtle rebellion, and her lip curls as she replies, 'I know the name of the sewer god.'

The sewer god. That's a new insult. Hades almost, almost, chuckles. 'Say it.'

She gazes up at him, her freckled face losing some of its composure, her mask of contempt crumbling to reveal the emotion beneath. 'Hades,' she whispers.

Mother, I'll never wake up from him...

Persephone considers him, plotting her next move. If he is indeed a king, then this is a game of chess. She refuses to play the part of the pawn. Let him see what he wants to see, what the others see – the frightened fawn, the babe in the wood – it will be a fatal mistake. Zeus underestimated her and Demeter misjudged her, as they do all springtime children, thinking them happy and vacant and drunk off nectar. Easy prey. Zeus had certainly thought so when he'd come upon her, frolicking in the spellflowers, and his intentions were as pure as the dirt he'd tried to bury her in. They're all so shocked when the pawn reveals itself as Queen.

Persephone conquers. She has spat in the faces of monsters and defied the will of gods. And here she crouches before the god of the underworld - the brother of Zeus, the idol, the rapist - and she makes her choice.

'And am I to be your prisoner here?'

Hades's platinum façade cracks a little at that – the beast has the audacity to smile. 'My prisoner? Hardly. You're my guest.'

I have already travelled too far...

A guest.

Preferable to a prisoner. Or prey.

She can work with guest.

Persephone gets to her feet, noticing that even at her full height, Hades dwarfs her. But she is far from cowed. She looks up at him – he isn't quite so monstrous once her eyes have had a chance to map his features, commit them to memory.

Her eyes rest, momentarily, on his bruise-black lips.

And Persephone smiles.

'Is it a custom in hell for guests to forage for their own food and water?' she enquires, and she skips off without waiting for an answer. Her shift rides up about her thighs again, sticky with sweat, but she can't bring herself to care. If she's already in hell, she might as well misbehave.

She grins to herself when she sees the lanky shadow of the monster unfold, begin to follow her.

Mute as smoke, as my first white dress...

She runs riot through the halls of Hades's palace – and that is what it is, there can be no other word to describe a place so ornate, every room festooned with trinkets, baroque fabrics and precious metals – until she comes to the dining room, an open hall with candelabras and a heaping feast set on the table. She comes to a halt at the head of the table, eyes wide as she takes in the array of foods, exotic ones she's never seen before. Clusters of plump black grapes and wedges of cheese, squiggled with electric-blue, goblets of mulberry wine and a strange, red globe-like fruit on a silver platter.

Hades lurks in the doorway behind her, but his presence, unlike his brother's, isn't ominous. It is oddly familiar, comforting even, and Persephone turns to him playfully, picking up one of the fruits and pretending to juggle it.

Hades watches her intently, solemnly, his violet eyes betraying a look of longing so fierce it's almost heartbreaking. 'Do you know the price for eating the fruits of the underworld?' he asks quietly.

Persephone stops juggling. Studies the fruit, then picks a knife up off the table and slices it into halves. It's a seeded fruit, its flesh white and stringy and resembling the ventricles of a heart, clogged with puce, wet pulp and tiny, glossy seeds, the colour of blood. Heartstones, love's labour made flesh.

And the spear of his name, once ferocious, dissolves on my tongue, like sugar, like birdsong…

She cups the halved pomegranate in one trembling hand. Seeds burst out of their vesicles, spilling over her fingers.

The seeds drape her wrist like jewels.

She counts them in pairs. Two, four, six, plucking at the crimson strands like the strings of a harp.

Her mother warned her not to eat the fruits of corruption. But oh, how she wants to be ruined.

She transfers the six seeds to her mouth and bites.

She tastes blood and sour cherries, and a note of something sweeter, more insidious. It's familiar.

All girls know the taste of innocence lost.

I whisper it: Hades.

Hades's claws close over the skin of her throat, a caress deeper and more intimate than any kiss. The bride of the monstrous bares her teeth in a bloody grin. 🌑

creative nonfiction

SHIT

MEILONI ERICKSON

Marleana should have had the forgotten, middle-child complex, but instead she was the pretty one, the center of attention, the belle of our *familia* of women.

It wasn't just her good looks either. She had a style about her. An energy. When *cholas* were in, my sister stood in the bathroom forever, aerosol Aqua-Net in one hand, the other hand holding a round bristle brush and bangs that reached for the sky. She's the one I called when I needed clothes advice. The one who knew about the new trends, or what would look good on your body shape. She was also seven years older than me, so it was almost inevitable that I wanted to be like her.

I cut my hair short in fourth grade to try and match her fashionable bob, but my curly mane would never lie flat. It fluffed where it should have been smooth, tangled where it should be sleek. Later, when I was thirteen, Marleana moved back home with Mom and me. I was an awkward middle school student and Marleana was a sexy young woman: independent, confident, beautiful. She had just turned twenty-one and spent her nights out, her mornings sleeping, and her afternoons working. She had a closet full of clothes I envied; silky dresses, sparkly tops, heels, jackets—everything a tween wants to wear but has no reason to. I would sneak into her room in the morning while she slept, careful not to bump her dresser covered in nail polishes and make-up, quietly sliding the door to her closet open and slipping out a shirt or a dress to wear inappropriately to school. I was already too big to fit into her pants. She'd always been the most petite of us girls, but she was so skinny by then that my size three waist was too big for her clothes. It made me feel fat and ugly.

I didn't know what meth was then. Or how it made you lose so much weight.

Her independence took another hit when she became pregnant a few months after she moved back home. Our Mom, who gave birth to her oldest at seventeen, was understandably upset. Sure, Marleana was twenty-one, working, and somewhat ready. It was her future baby-daddy, Jose Garcia, that was the problem. One thing that my mother especially hated, was when he'd park his primer-gray, old-school wagon in front of our apartment building, right below my sister's window, and crank oldies until she came down to talk to him. I remember my mom yelling at Marleana about what a loser he was as the chords of Otis Redding's "These Arms of Mine" could be heard coming through the front windows.

A few weeks later, she moved in with the Garcias, who shortened her name from Marleana to Marlena. A subtle difference, just dropping an A, but it changed her name's pronunciation. Made it sound more Mexican. I was at the hospital when her first son was born. I saw her exhausted beauty as she held her little miracle. She was glowing brighter than ever before, sweaty hair pulled up in a messy bun, stragglers sticking to her neck. It made me think maybe, someday.

By the time her second son was born (barely a year later), things had changed. I wasn't living with Mom anymore, didn't make it to the hospital to see my sister in the glory of motherhood. She had the baby thirty minutes after arriving at the hospital and was released the same day. Without Mom around, I didn't see my sister and the babies very often. Occasionally, Marleana would call Grandma's house, where I was staying, and let us know everything was going well. And sometimes she'd stop by with the boys, but not Jose. I would coo and tickle the babies while Grandma tried to get Marleana to eat.

"Oh, you're so thin, *mija*," our grandmother would say to Marleana. "*Flacca*. Eat something. Let me make you *un burrito*. A *tosdada*?"

"No, Grandma, I'm good. I just ate."

"Just a little something? I have some *puerco con chile*, I'll make you a little *taco*. You need strength for these boys."

"No, really. I'm fine."

My junior year I started partying with my friends on the weekends, and as most high schoolers our main goal was often to get alcohol or weed. My sister was a good source for both. I would go over to the Garcia's, often with my best friend who had a car, and pick up my sister and take her to the store with us. She was always so happy to see me, but never really wanted me to get out of the car and go inside the house. The first time I did, I understood why.

Years before, Jose had begun building a shed, and as his sons began to arrive, he worked to complete it. They were now living in the incomplete room. The structure itself was sound, with a roof and everything, but the inside was unfinished: no insulation, bare plywood floors, and an extension cord that served as electricity. I had dropped by without her knowing I was coming and could tell she was a little flustered at my arrival.

"This is temporary, just until Jose finds another job," she told me.

"Sure," I agreed.

"It's not that bad really, we have a little space heater going at night. It gets hot in here."

I didn't know what to say to that, so I just nodded. She had her oldest boy out there with her, and he played on the bed running Crayolas over sheets of notebook paper, making full page rainbows in the wrong colors.

"So what have you been up to?" I asked.

"Oh, you know, taking care of the boys. Joseph is inside sleeping right now. He spends a lot of time inside with Graciela."

"Cool."

"Yeah, it's nice."

> She had white tennis shoes next to her, and she picked up a white-out pen, and she began coloring the rubber bottoms of the sneakers.

As we spoke my sister had gotten comfortable on the floor, leaning up against the mattress and box springs. She had white tennis shoes next to her, and she picked up a white-out pen, like the ones I had used in middle school to paint my nails, and she began coloring the rubber bottoms of the sneakers.

"Is that how you keep your shoes so white?" I asked. Her stuff always retained that new quality, while mine looked worn within hours of the first wear.

"Yeah, I hadn't done it before. One of Jose's friends told me about it."

"Smart."

When we talked about that day later, after she got clean, Marleana would cringe. She'd say 'Maaaaaaan. I was tweaking so hard then.' But I didn't see it. Our family had never lived in a converted shed, but we had definitely been through hard times. I thought my sister and her new family were in transition, about to get a house of their own. I didn't notice the slightly chemically, plastic smell, or the bits of straws and burnt spoons. I didn't think of the pimples on my sister's face as speed bumps, but as a bad breakout. I didn't know that at the time, San Bernardino County was known as the Meth capital of the U.S. I didn't understand that statistic in relation to my family. I didn't see that my sister was an addict.

It wasn't until the next year, right after my eighteenth birthday, that I began to see. I was back with Mom then, we were living in a cute house, not far from Grandma. Marleana's first few days with us she slept. Like seventy-two hours straight. I mean, she was up at some points (the boys were staying with us, too), but I just remember her in a pile of blankets in the corner of the living room. I don't remember if Mom took time off work to help; I'm sure I must have babysat here and there, but mostly I remember how dirty Marleana was.

One night, soon after she was with us, I came back from getting street tacos with a friend. We were sitting down to eat, when Marleana woke up.

"Hey, Sis. You hungry?" I asked.

She nodded, and I passed over the foil packet that contained my four tacos. "Grab one," I said.

She nodded again and started eating. My friend and I snuck out back to smoke pot before we ate, and when we came back inside all my food was gone.

"You ate them all?" I asked, annoyance clear in my tone.

"Yeah, sorry. They were soo good," she answered as she slunk back to her corner and into her pile of blankets.

I was pissed. This bitch ate all my tacos! I didn't understand then that she hadn't eaten in in who knew how long. That those little tacos were the first bit of nourishment her body had had in far too long. I still feel guilty whenever I think about it.

Days passed. She was having a hard time getting herself together. My sister, my pretty sister, who always fixed herself, now lived in sweats, her long beautiful hair tied haphazardly into a ponytail of knots.

"You have to shower," Mom told her.

"No!" Marleana would yell in a petulant child voice.

"Yes, Rochelle. Now." Mom uses middle names when she means business. "I'm starting the shower, you better get in in five minutes."

It was evening. The boys were in the living room, watching Disney movies, while Mom tried to bring her daughter back.

"C'mon, Sis," I told her. "Just a real quick one. I'll brush your hair after."

"Uuuuuhhhhhh!" But she got up and went to the bathroom.

It was almost an hour before she got out. She came into my room wrapped in the large bath sheets that Mom favored and plopped on my bed. I was on the floor, pretending to do homework while really watching TV.

"How was it?" I asked.

"Warm."

I nodded. Her hair was wrapped in a towel, turban style, and only her arms, ankles, and feet were visible. She had shaved, I could see little rivets of water mixed with a hint of blood run down her legs. As I watched one trickle down to her feet, I noticed her toes. The nails were long and ragged. Broken into points on some toes and grown so long on others that they curled over the tips. Small blotches of metallic blue nail polish were present here and there, but it had obviously been a long time since she had paid any attention.

"You want me to do your toes?"

She was lying back on my bed now, her legs crossed at the ankle. "No way!" she said, pulling her legs up and hiding her feet in the folds of the bath sheet.

"C'mon, you need a pedi." I playfully grabbed for her feet but she twisted, rolling away.

"Uh-uh, they're gross. Shit comes out of your toes." She always called meth "Shit". Like she wanted to disassociate what it really was.

"All the more reason to clean 'em up." I got up and went to my dresser where I kept all of my polishes. I grabbed them and tossed them on the bed. "Pick a color." I went to the hall and got all the supplies: polish remover, clippers, files.

When I came back in she was sitting up again, her feet planted on the floor. She had a red bottle of polish in her hands and didn't say anything as she handed it over.

I went to work. Her feet were kind of gross, and I am kind of squeamish, but it didn't bother me. First I cleaned each toe with remover, making sure to reach in the creases where polish and grit like to hide. Then I went for the clippers and began trimming. As I reached the second and third toe on her left foot, I noticed the nails fell apart as I tried to cut them. They were brittle, like a dry pie crust. And the nubs of skin right below the nail were like callouses. I ran my thumb over the nails and skin, feeling the rough surface. The calloused skin feeling like a buffer between my fingers and my sister's toes.

"I told you, Shit comes out of your toes." She had noticed my fascination.

"No worries. I'm gonna make your toes so pretty, you won't even notice."

We didn't talk as I worked. Mostly my sister lay back, watching the ceiling while I attempted to revive some of her beauty. I worked hard, peeling layer and layer of skin from the dry toe tips, never finding smooth skin, trying to clean the pain, and the tired, and the Shit out of my sister.

"Alright, finished!" I said with a flourish.

My sister lifted her feet to admire her toes without having to get up. "They look good," she said after a second. She sat up, placing her feet gently on the floor, keeping her toes off the ground. "You can still kinda see where they're fucked up but it's not that bad." She leaned over and touched her fingers to the tips of her dry toes. Wiggling them so they sparkled in the lamplight.

"Yeah, and they'll be back to normal before you know it." I grabbed her foot and gave it a little shake as I got up to return all the supplies.

"Maybe," she said. "Maybe."

THERE IS A MAN WITH FIFTY HEADS AND A HUNDRED HANDS

CASH MYRON TOKLAS

There is a man with fifty heads and a hundred hands
Who lies under the bed
And a one-eyed man beneath the floor.
It has been this way for as long as any of my children can remember,
And my children are now grown,
swallowed,
vomited,
and grown some more.

There is a man with fifty heads and a hundred hands who lies under the bed
And a one-eyed man beneath the floor.
Lua, the goddess of destruction, wipes her yellow cheek against the windowpane
And tells me that I should be afraid.
Rhea, my wife, tells me that I should be afraid
Of the goddess of destruction who wipes her yellow cheek against the windowpane.

There is a man with fifty heads and a hundred hands who lies under the bed,
A one-eyed man beneath the floor,
And a goddess of destruction who wipes her yellow cheek against the windowpane.
And I am afraid
Not of them
But of the children
Whom I have swallowed
And vomited
But who have now grown some more.

HOW I LOST THE WAR

CASH MYRON TOKLAS

You smell the abyss before you see him. Tartarus enters you like a truck
backing into your nostrils. Blink and he's inside you. It wasn't always like this.

When I was small, Tartarus was the primordial who sucked kites out of the sky
and hid lost toys in a hole drilled deep into the basement floor.

I peered up at him until the sun poked little holes around my retina.
I peered down at him until the basement walls closed in.

Tartarus was the one who helped me pin the one-eyed man beneath the floor
and the hundred-handed man under the bed. He was also the one who threatened to release them.

Later, Tartarus was the vice principal to whom the misbehaved were sent.
I looked the abyss in the eye. He stared me down, grabbed my shoulder, threw me to the ground.

Then he was a state of mind, the windowless prison that shackled me
from inside. Every surface became a mirror that reflects my shame.

I saw him as a bloodlessness about my face. The prisoner slope in my shoulders,
the sense of an unpleasant ending. The children saw him. The war was over before it began.

Finally, the abyss became a place, an assisted living facility across the water,
and I am waiting for my children to put me on the ferry.

The One-Eyed Man Who Sleeps Beneath the Floor

CASH MYRON TOKLAS

The one-eyed man who sleeps beneath the floor,
The secret king who hides deep in the woods:
Each has a mission we choose to ignore,
Each plots a coupe d'état while we just brood.

HESTIA

CASH MYRON TOKLAS

Forever it seems
I have dreamt of Hestia
burning
like the hearth she tends
softly, cruelly
ribbons in her hair
a shaft of light
across her face
betrayed
inflamed in the
dream of Freud or
Manchester by the
Sea in a room locked
beside my own as I
slept and unhearing
heard her call When
I would never let her
burn in the flames
but would instead
devour her
not like teeth
sinking & tearing into
flesh & masticating
but rather a suffocation
envelopment &
disappearance
like I did with my
other children only to
vomit them out
again.

THE CHAOS OF CHILDBIRTH

CASH MYRON TOKLAS

We're drinking whiskey and playing cards. It's my brother Japetus and me. I'm doing most of the drinking. After all, it's my wife who's in the delivery room. We're expecting Chaos. Uncle Hypnos walks in and takes a seat. Japetus says, "When my wife was pregnant, I went hunting. Now guys feel like they have to sit around the hospital drinking whiskey." Uncle Hypnos snorts. "When your Aunt Pasithea was expecting," he says, "I told the doctor to just knock us both out until the whole thing was over." I laugh, but he isn't joking. He closes his eyes and falls asleep. Now Grandpa Erebus walks in. Japetus pour him a drink and catches him up on the conversation. Erebus says, "When Grandma Nix was pregnant, we didn't have anesthesia. Nix just cast a great darkness over the world. When it cleared, I could hear the babies crying." With that, everything goes dark. A loud cold blast of clanging entropy rocks the room. Hypnos wakes with a start. Even in the darkness, we can tell that Chaos is among us. I struggle to my feet and say, "Great Grandfather Chaos, what was childbirth like in your day?" The entropy clangs again. Chaos says, "In my day, there were no women, no whiskey, no hunting, no darkness, no sleep. I did all the work, and I did it in tohu va-vohu." The shaking stops. Chaos continues, "All children come from Chaos and are sworn to serve me. When they forget their vows, we call your Uncle Thanatos." A doctor appears and announces, "It's a boy." We let out a whoop and follow the doctor through the birthing center, stumbling in darkness, buffeted by wind. Squinting, I see Rhea, my wife, holding the baby blanketed in wool. She hands the package to me. Chaos shakes again. Chairs fly to the ceiling. Windows smash. "We'll name him Zeus," Rhea says. I take the package, stuff it in my mouth, and swallow. A nursemaid darts around the corner, another package in her arms.

poetry

MELTDOWN

RC DEWINTER

lost in a
bottle of jack i
never saw
the first night
the sun never set. when i
sobered up the street

was full of
everyone, waving
their arms and
talking a
mile a minute, kids crying,
the saintly ranting

the end of
the world while dogs barked
in three-part
harmony
and far-off sirens wailed in
their useless distress.

i hadn't
lived expecting to
witness the
end of the
world, a balloon melting in
the judas kiss of

gold, that false
god people chased with
no thought of
betrayal.

i laughed and left the lost to
their madness, knowing

i had that
half-full bottle to
carry me
over the
the threshold of sentience
into the puddle.

counting the
coins in my pouch, i
grinned as the
silver, a
a glittering snake, smiled back.
eyes closed, i waited.

poetry

CARD TRICK

RC DEWINTER

you accuse me
of being a magician
but that is not the case

i merely riffle the cards
to show what is possible
it involves no special skill

only the willingness to use
the legerdemain of truth
which is after all

a paste of what truly is
and the ingredients
with which you season it

you will see and taste one thing
the person next to you another
i am not the magician

the magician is you

THE CONFESSION THAT NEVER WAS

RC DEWINTER

sultry summer wrapped me
in her pitiless embrace
it fevered me with thoughts of manflesh
naked sweaty
mine to devour

images beyond erotic flickered
through my brain colliding with
the years of deprivation
a trainwreck of desire unfulfilled

suddenly ashamed
i felt the need for absolution
an uncharacteristic urge to spill
collected decades of secret sin
and so sought out a priest

but everything was different
no claustrophobic booth
no sliding panel with an anonymous ear
ready to receive the darkness of the soul

i was admitted to an office light and bright
with nothing of the religious about it
but for one plain wooden cross and a few
generic feelgood posters on the walls

behind a desk there sat a man
and yes he wore the collar
hello i'm father richard come and sit
he gestured to a chair across from his

i felt nothing of the sacred
only for all the world as if
i were applying for a job
or had come to buy insurance

and that at least made sense
for what is this unburdening
but bargaining with god for penance
and one's proper place in heaven

i couldn't sit here face to face and spill
the secrets of my soul
this was too much of a salvation burger to chew

so making my excuses
i excused myself from this dry interview
and once outside looked up into
that summer sky where angels with
their flaming swords awaited

it made me think of all the wars
that were never waged and all the ones that were
and my how body was a battlefield of
unforgiven sins and the good intentions
paving that famous road

i saw black rain falling on hiroshima
heads on pikes and piles of corpses
lying in a ditch
there were bodies in the trees
nooses wrapped round bulging necks

they forgave me for reviving them
i've never killed or tortured anyone
or stolen anything
with the exception of a few unwary hearts
that truth be told were begging to be stolen

my sins
victimless crimes

tattooed on the skin of my conscience
require no absolution

LADIES LUNCH

RC DEWINTER

we had company for lunch today
two women
one i know
and have always thought a bitch
another i had met only once before

these were not guests of my choosing
but being a guest myself
in the house where i am staying
was perforce obliged to be civil

we sat at a dining table
set with all the best
they chattered
these two and the hostess
all through the meal
trivialities
of the lowest common denominator

i was mostly silent
having no interest in any of it
nor able to add anything polite
to the conversation

over coffee
the woman
whom i had met only once before
stared at me intently
i stared back

finally she spoke
i remember you
you're the artist

the poet
the singer
the witch

i nodded silently as she continued
you're a bit odd
she said
you spent an age
warning me of the dangers of BPA
and global warming
the hypocrisy of religion
the dangers of creeping corporatism
not very artistic of you
no poetry in that conversation
you were rather a johnny-one-note
all doom and gloom

she waved an overly-jewelled hand
and laughed dismissively
ah well
she concluded
it takes all kinds doesn't it

her companion
the bitch
laughed with her
both of them smug in their normality

i smiled
all was civilized politesse
until they saw my fangs

we had company for lunch today
they were delicious

CHRISTMAS PLAY

RC DEWINTER

when the puppet show was over
there was a general stampede
toward the swinging exit doors
though angels were singing
and the halls were decked with holly
there was no christian charity
in that theater full of the damned

when the maddened mass
of bodies realized the doors
no longer swung but were instead
padlocked leaving them burning
like those triangle shirtwaist girls left
blackened bald and broken
in a world not far from this one

and blood flowed hot and bright

the theater critics
most of whom were innocent of all
but showing up to rate the show
for a penny a word
became
unlike those sealed doors
unhinged

and as the heat increased the floors
were greased with the melting insincerity
of those whose tongues were paid to write
as cheating couples clutched each other
hastily swallowing every secret between them
the falling of the weak unloosed a
flood of bending on the part of those

still standing
stooping to retrieve the baubles dropped
while by the pitiless doors
the men pretending to be practical
tried various techniques to free them
but fights erupted
jealousies and spite
jeering at the native origins
of their rapidly unravelling bespoke suits

and in the midst of all the squabbling
those traitorous doors flew open
blowing in a cloud of mighty trumpets
played by doubledealing strumpets
and withered every foreign and domestic heart
still beating

the herald of judgment had arrived

when all the flags fell from the wall
everyone still breathing
blackened canaries in a coal mine
knew all was lost

and each in wretched trembling voice
sang in a different key
a different tempo
but in the end
the melody was the same

and across the world in his well appointed study
the puppetmaster took another sip of mashed potatoes
smiling grimly at the carnage beaming down
from the great walls
huge flat screens revealing all

JAWS

OWEN LUBOZYNSKI

It took the death of my father to startle me into humanity,
make me wonder what speechless terror coursed
like an astringent through the blood of the wildebeest
in the PBS nature documentary – though there was,
I think, no terror in my father's passing, which was not
the rending conclusion of a desperate chase
but the consummation of the union between a man
and the ruin drawn into his body's blueprint.
I had not wondered at those shades of blue,
that soft, ineluctable twilight. I was a creature
red in tooth and thought. I always rooted for the lioness.
I panted along with the gaunt, fleet cheetah, exulted
in the dire plunge of the peregrine falcon, reveled
in the menace of the great, white shark, its monstrosity,
a grandeur more compelling than the sweet,
painstaking little marvels troubled up by human hands.
And then the *anglerfish*. Stark nightmare
of nature. How the female baited her naïve neighbors
with her headlamp, swallowed them whole
with a thrilling suddenness – the authority of her jagged
under-bite. How the puny male spent his puny
independence in a starving search for her and how,
once he'd found her at last, he compulsively nibbled
at her flank until her flesh dissolved his face,
consumed him, leaving only his gonads protruding
for the purposes of insemination, at her later convenience.
I liked that there was no fucking lesson in that.
I liked how the anglerfish slouched through the deep
like a mobile abyss with a porch light.
I did not fear the nightfall that lurked in the ocean,
stalked the savannah, scourged the far reaches of the sky.
But then the void opened in my living room,
swallowed my father clean out of his body,

leaving not so much as a bruise upon it,
and I knew then that I carried that greedy mouth within me,
that we all do, that we must handle each other
with such terrible gentleness,
lest the tickling of our careless jostles trigger the hinge of that jaw to snap
shut.

FEMME FELIX

OWEN LUBOZYNSKI

She lies. She lines her lips.
She rips into the etiquette
of a bougie brunch
with comments in turn
mordant, incisive, sanguine,
sanguinary,
bites off the matter with a smile
but eyes the remnants
on the others' plates.
Her palate is precise but not
discriminating.
She'll try anything once.
Though you may be outré,
you'll be no more than
an hors d'ouvre to her,
even as you protest that you
deserve to be savored,
heave yourself like an offering
across her threshold.
She will not open her arms
to you, but she may
unhinge her jaw.
Like some creeping things
that thrived before Adam,
she has been known to spit
on her prey,
that the acid of her discernment
may tenderize her meal
before it touches her tongue.

PERVERSIONS

OWEN LUBOZYNSKI

Sometimes my lust insists on repulsive objects,
prods me like an incessant elbow to the boob.
The complacent, lank-haired man who got up at the last
open mic and delivered, in a booming monotone,
a seemingly endless "short" story embellished
with multiple, gratuitous sexual assaults sits down
next to me. I loathe him, but my system mistranslates
that emotion, reverses the polarity. My skin
wants to touch his gross hair. My skin wants
to crawl away from itself. It has been so long
since it has been touched by anyone.
It's beyond hungry, would eat just about anything
at this point but knows better than to gnaw
at something who might actually fill me up.
As a teenager, I wore a rubber band on my wrist
for snapping to chastise errant desires.
At the time, I viewed all titillation as repulsive –
for the same reason we wretch at the stench
of spoiled meat: because it could kill us.
I was a child. I was supposed to become an adult.
But an adult would have been a different
person. Therefore, the child would no longer
be. Therefore, the child would die. Therefore
I snapped the rubber band, to keep myself alive.
I am adult now, so I guess it didn't work.
Someone kissed me there, on the wrist, once.
I loved her at the time. I do not love her now.
I suppose many of me have died.
I am a cemetery dripping with vines, thicketed,
nearly impassable, and I wish a couple
would sneak in at dusk and fuck against the mausoleum.
When my breasts started budding, I thought
they were tumors. I died and was buried

in my chest. I was buried between my hips.
Someone found me with a finger once,
and I screamed bloody murder. I want to nibble
on the bad writer's hair. One of me
is punishing me. Or they all are, for letting them
end like this, un-eulogized, with no one
to visit their graves. My crotch is haunted.
Only the brave and the foolish dare enter.
I can't have company until I dispel the spirts.
But it would be so lonely in here without me.

WOLF MAN

J. V. BIRCH

In t-shirts & shorts
he's covered in hair he can't shake.

It ripples his skin
like it's caught on something

creeping in the dark.
He feels the teeth in his head

the growl in his throat
the moon rising to rip out his heart.

The girl sitting next to him smiles.
He doesn't return it

notes the pulse in her neck
can almost taste what moves there.

His bones start to sing

OUR PREDATORS

EMMA WYNN

The swim team practices every afternoon at three,
all the beautiful boys living Davids
posed and peacocking
in their spandex Temple of echoes,
a shampoo commercial head-flip of wet hair out of eyes
mounting ladders one-handed,
surging up like suns.
This winter they dare each other to carve swastikas on desks,
take to heiling each other in hallways,
gleeful thrusts and knowing glances that send my heart scuttling -
all my tattoos condensing to numbers.
This is how we laugh now, they say.

We meant to give them other gods
than money and clear skin.
In our books, charts absolve the poor,
but we cheer their war games in pool, field, class
knowing we swim with sharks.
We prize their teeth,
forget our tender underbellies -
live vicariously Leviathan.
Side-by-side,
we, who meant to gentle them,
they, who burn to devour.

short story

PERICARDIUM

EMILY HARRISON

He's watching her from the wardrobe in the spare room, eye set against a crack in the door, wide enough to peer carefully through. He's hoping for answers - she's been hiding something in the room for a day or two, sneaking up there alone. He has nothing so far, not that he's watched her for long. She's sat on her heels, feet bare and dusty on the Persian rug, playing with a soft toy doll. She doesn't know he's there – he's sure of it.

He waits a little longer, five minutes, maybe less, and then she moves, wriggling around to sit cross-legged, shuffling over and off the end of the rug, discarding the doll to her left. He squints as she pulls up the corner of the tatty material, folding it over gently. The floorboards below are darker, unbleached by the sun.

Her fingers search the edges of a loose floorboard. She grips at the sides of it with her nails, lifting slowly.

"Hello," she whispers into the hole, floorboard placed to the side.

The thick wood of the wardrobe creaks with his weight as he cleans closer, knees aching. She curves her head like an owl to seek out the nose, her thumb locked in her mouth, a nervous habit she's had since she was an infant. He leans away from the doors, crouching down quietly, shrinking back from the sliver of light, hand over his mouth. Seconds pass in silence. He holds his breath a little longer before rising up to peer through the crack once again. She's facing the hole in the floor, her body is covering it, the doll back in her hands.

He observes, anticipating an explanation. But all she does is whisper "hello" into the floor twice more before sighing and straightening herself up to stand.

She hums as she leaves the room, the floorboard in place, the rug laid neat. When he checks her hiding hole, he finds only the bones of a miniscule animal and a teddy bear with its left arm missing.

He does not watch her from the wardrobe the next day, but he pays close attention. His sister is a creature of habit. She visits the room three times, various items tucked into her chequered dress pockets; a yoyo, a handful of crayons, and something wet, staining the thin material of her dress in a damp circle. The summer is sticky and close, the farmhouse rife with spiders and dust – every time she returns from clambering up the stairs to visit her secret, she is ruddy with the heat.

He questions her in the kitchen later in the evening, both of them spilling crumbs on the linoleum from sharing a plate of buttered crackers. The sun is swelling down to a blur behind the hills that sit on the horizon, framed though the window like a Pissarro painting. Dad is in the garden, hammering nails into a snapped section of fence – his back bare and sweaty.

"What are you hiding upstairs?"

The thumb makes its way to her mouth. When she was a baby, he'd try to stop her from chewing by yanking it away, the skin catching on her baby teeth. He watches instead. Being six years older than his four-year-old sister lends itself to fresh strength he cannot always grasp. She refuses to reply.

"I know there's something up there, in the floor."

She removes the thumb and replaces it with a half-eaten cracker.

"If you don't tell me I'll tell Dad."

He knows, as he says it, that it'll do little to sway her. Dad has the ability to appear opaque and transparent in equal measure – his presence more ghostlike than paternal. She shrugs and swallows, taking a sip of watery orange juice and hopping down from the table.

"If you don't tell me I'll tell Mum."

That holds her, half-way past the kitchen counter.

"You can't."

He tells her he can. He will. Mum is buried in the next village over, having died shortly after his sister's birth. They visit every couple of months, speaking to her through the ground.

Her blonde brows furrow.

"No, you can't" she pauses, "I've already told her."

She says it petulantly, and spins on her heel, wandering back into the bowels of the house – the corridor to the kitchen dark despite the evening light.

A week passes, and he discovers little more than what he's already witnessed. There are some new items – items she's snuck in without him noticing; a dead frog, a pile of cut grass, and a mug of water. His sister once hid a bird in her doll house until it withered away, too young to fully grasp that animals need sustenance, not a pink plastic home made for miniature people.

The wardrobe beckons him tonight – another sweltering evening of their late July summer. The air in the farmhouse is thick – enough to cup, shape and contort if the elements allowed. Life has slowed to an agitated crawl. He wipes his top lip of salted sweat and sets his eye against the crack.

9:12 PM and she enters. She should be in bed. So should he. He can see his watch face in the low light. She drops down a brown paper bag from the local grocers and reaches for the floorboard, folding over the rug. From her position – body hovering over the hole, bag in front of her – there is little he can observe.

He listens instead.

As she did the week previous, she whispers down below – "hello". Paper rustles and is discarded to the side, the contents between her fingers – he can tell by the way her elbows are bent. The room stills as she whispers again, and then it appears, whatever it is, for she sighs out a "you scared me, silly" and giggles, leaning further forward, her pyjama t-shirt riding a little up her back. A dull thud; the item dropped. She sits up, extends her legs back and sets herself out flat on her belly, face flush to the floor, peering inside.

A drop of sweat slips off his brow and down into the crook of his nose.

"Sorry I didn't come see you earlier, I was busy."

She'd spent the better part of the afternoon running around in the garden chasing bees, before disappearing towards the marsh near the bottom field.

"I hope you like it?"

Her head dips further in. His eye is beginning to sting – he blinks and rubs.

She talks then, spilling out anecdotes of her day, what she's eaten, the teddies in her room; the adventures they might have taken whilst she was out. He's about to sit down, tired and confused, when she quickly rolls onto her back and sits up, staring directly towards the wardrobe. If he didn't know better, he could swear she was looking straight through to him. She sneezes instead, three times, then returns to talking into the hole.

The last week of July falls away to early August and the summer turns close and moist. The wardrobe is his home once again. Dad is out, buying rings of barb wire for the outhouse, so he's been left in charge, a responsibility he ignores. She is in the garden, but he knows she'll come to nourish her secret. It's nearing lunchtime.

He runs a fingernail down his hand as he waits, digging it in where his thumb meets his palm, the affectation for calmness slowly dissipating. He counts out the days since the secret first appeared. Thirteen. He's yet to uncover the truth.

A slam down below indicates her presence. As she makes her way upstairs, she begins to call out, small voice carrying in the echo of the high beams.

"Simon."

He holds a breath.

"Siiiiiimon," she sing-songs.

Doors open upstairs – his room, her room, Dad's too.

"Simon?"

He holds himself still – the spare room her final destination. She doesn't call out to him again. She huffs instead and then grins, heading straight to the rug. A quick prod of the floor, rug and wood lifted, "hello" whispered. She is empty handed.

The finger running scratch marks into his hand begins again, moving slow and quiet. She lays flat, head propped on her elbow, speaking into the hole.

"Hello. No food today – couldn't find anything."

Her feet are bare and muddy, as though she's being trampling in the overgrown marsh.

From the angle of her body he can see the black recess of the oblong hole. Her arm reaches inside, and she replies to a question he's unsure she was asked.

"Dunno", she sucks her bottom lip between her milk teeth, "he must be outside. "I'll show you to him soon."

His nail has started working deeper, biting.

She moves her arm back and forth, back and forth, reaching in deep.

"You want to come out today?"

Silence.

"It'll be okay."

Her face drops closer as if to submerge.

"Come on, Mummy, don't be scared."

When he was younger Dad took him to swim in a river – the May afternoon cloudless. The water was ice-cold and as Dad stripped down to his boxers and waded in, he, in his aqua shoes and tiger t-shirt, remained crouched on a stepping stone, dipping his fingers in and out of the cool. Dad pulled him in a few minutes later, the shock making his whole body stop, panic prickling across him. That fear – acute and intense, is palpable within the room.

His sister calls "Mummy" again and then reduces her voice to a whisper, "come on."

Her hands delve inside and disappear. When they resurface they are not alone. Wrapped from wrist to shoulder is a snake – thin and olive in colour. She lifts it gently and sits back, gazing openly at the animal. It nudges its oval head against the birthmark on her cheek softly and runs itself along her jaw, its underbelly a burnt coal white. It winds over her neck, coasting from her arm, and begins coiling up through her hair, stark against the blonde. She is smiling, stroking at the scales as it goes, holding both hands steady. It reaches her crown, tail at her spine. He can take no more of the scene and bursts from the wardrobe, tumbling through the doors.

He hears himself shout, though he's not sure what he says, and the snake falters, dropping to her shoulder. His sister freezes.

Collapsed on his knees, his skin cut on the floor, he sets his eyes upon it. The wardrobe door swings back on its hinges. There is blood beneath his right knee. It hisses and glides out, body propped in the dust ridden air, contorted in the shape of an L, tail wound round his sister's neck for support. It cocks its head to the side, as does his sister, almost mechanical in motion, the snake setting loose its black tongue, before calling it back – inquest over benevolence. Her tongue is sable too, his sisters, as though she's rubbed coal along the flesh.

"It's just mummy, Simon," she says, mouth dark, small eyes now watching the snake reel from its stance. "Say hello." •

short story

GUILT

MEGAN SCHMID

Trent sat on the curb, his head in hands covered in the woman's blood. They painted streaks of red on his face, left chunks of human flesh in his hair. He thought, maybe if he squeezed his eyes shut, pressed on his eyeballs hard enough, the images might disappear. Seeing the woman run into the street. Getting out of the car and running back to where she lay, body broken, in the middle of the intersection. Rolling her over, seeing half her face crushed, one eye popped out of its socket, her body jerking, involuntary spasms, a final shuddering breath. Even if he gouged his own eyes out, he knew the images were permanent.

"Sir, excuse me," the cop said, standing over Trent, the flashing lights of the cop car painting his face in red and blue. "I need to get your statement."

Trent detached himself from the magnetic pull of the curb and for a moment thought he would fall back down, his legs struggling under the weight of his guilt.

"Arrest me. It's my fault," Trent said. Confession supposedly unburdened the soul. He wasn't Catholic, had never practiced admitting his failings to another, and was disappointed when the feeling of responsibility wasn't lifted.

"Sir, let's just start from the beginning," the cop said, his laser eyes focusing their beam of intimidation on him. "Tell me your name"

"Trent McDonnell."

"Ok, Mr. McDonnell, which direction were you coming from?"

"I was going east on Fulton," Trent said, taking a deep breath.

The cop nodded for him to continue.

"I was approaching the intersection at 43rd Avenue. I wasn't speeding. I swear. I never speed here at night. She, the woman, ran into the crosswalk as I entered the intersection. I swear I didn't see her. Not until…" He got distracted by flashes. "Are those really necessary? I'm confessing." The other cops set out markers and took pictures of the evidence, of the crime scene.

"Sir, currently, you are not under arrest. I advise you to continue recounting the accident. Specifically, the facts."

"Umm. Where was I?" Trent asked looking to the cop, stalling. In those intimidating laser beams for eyes, Trent found moments of blissful blankness. Maybe he could draw this exchange out indefinitely.

"She entered the crosswalk, and you did what?" he reminded Trent.

"Do you know who she is…was?"

"Don't worry about that now. Right now, I need you to continue giving your statement."

Trent looked at his hands. Was that brain under his fingernails? "Umm…she ran into the crosswalk. I didn't see her until I hit her. Well, I mean, until a second before I hit her. There was no time for me to stop."

"Your Honor, he is an upstanding citizen with no record," said Jeff Benson, Trent's lawyer, a friend from college. A friend who insisted on representing Trent despite his protests. Jeff continued, "The intersection where the vehicular incident occurred was a known blind spot. The bushes on that side of the street were overgrown. Kara Thompson was crossing against the light. My client, Trent McDonnell was entering the intersection on a green light going the speed limit. This was an accident, plain and simple. Today, he is pleading guilty to vehicular manslaughter. I request you take all of this into consideration when sentencing him."

"Trent McDonnell," said the Honorable Judge Waller. "I am sentencing you to four hundred hours of community service, a five thousand dollar fine and one-year probation."

Trent looked up from his hands, fingers interlaced, each cutting off circulation to the others. He avoided looking up until now because Kara Thompson stood behind the judge passing her own sentence. After the accident, a short article appeared in the Chronicle with a picture of the beautiful twenty-two-year-old UC art student, Kara Thompson, showing off her smile, her dark curly hair, lips stretched across her too white teeth. But that's not how Trent saw her standing behind the judge. She stood there, her skull caved in, brains leaking out the cracks, one eyeball out of its socket, the other bloodshot. Hers was the real judgement and the sentence was life in the prison of his guilt.

The first night, the night of the accident, he woke from a succession of nightmares. Kara Thompson was standing on Joanne's side of the bed, staring at him, dripping blood onto Joanne's sleeping form. Trent got out of bed, knowing sleep would not return, and went to the kitchen. Kara joined him for coffee. He thought a run might help him chase sleep. So, he dressed, but she chased him, blood drops trailing behind her. He tried to out run her, but she was just as fast, no matter how fast he went. Then he ran through the park. He stopped at that intersection and tried to drop her off.

"This is where you left your body," he told her. She didn't look anywhere except at him.

The next day he found the article in the Chronicle, the one that gave her name and the picture. He began stalking her on-line and in person. That is, if it's possible to stalk a dead woman. She needed to move on, go to the other side, find heaven. He wanted to help her do that.

He went to her funeral. Lurking on the fringes, afraid to offend the mourners, he tried to drop her off at the church and the graveyard. Her family recounted her life, her childhood antics, her adult dreams and ambitions. She didn't seem to care. She had eyes, eye really, only for him.

> He went to her funeral. Lurking on the fringes, he tried to drop her off at the church and the graveyard.

While on probation, when he wasn't picking up trash on the side of the road, he continued to research her life, her favorite foods, favorite restaurants, previous boyfriends, current friends. He went everywhere that Kara loved to go. He thought if she went one more time, she might move on. At first, he brought Joanne along, but soon realized two's company, three's a crowd. Besides, he got the feeling Kara didn't like his girlfriend much. And every night since the first night, Kara stood on Joanne's side of the bed and dripped blood on the quilt. When Joanne moved out, Kara climbed in.

Trent stopped driving. He sold the car, gave it away really because who wants to pay for a car with dead woman's brains stuck to the undercarriage. He took the bus and everywhere he went his second shadow, Kara, came too.

Once, Trent took Kara to her old apartment. They watched her boyfriend leave in the morning, eyes bloodshot from crying, or from drinking too much. It was hard to tell. "See," he told her. "Look how much he loves and misses you. Maybe you should stay with him. It might help him mourn you." A lock of her curly hair fell off onto the sidewalk, bits of scalp still clinging to it. That was all she left for the boyfriend; the rest she took home with Trent.

On another day Trent discovered the dead woman had a sense of humor. He was walking behind her best friend, when a cop car pulled up next to him. "Mr. McDonnell," said the cop.

"You have to stop following Ms. Edgerly. If you persist, I will arrest you." Kara smiled, a hideous sight — lips wide, jaw hanging askew.

When Trent's probation was over, he took a trip to her home town. He thought nostalgia might trap her attention long enough for him to escape. He tried to buy her a seat on the plane, but the airline refused to sell a ticket to a dead woman. She made it through security and onto the plane anyway. She sat in an empty seat across the aisle from him and only left a little blood on the seat back.

"Is this where you went to school?" he asked her while sitting in the stands of the football field. "Did you kiss your first boyfriend under these bleachers?" She wasn't interested. Her one functional eye, the blood-shot one, stared at him unblinking, never leaving his face.

Desperate to get rid of her, Trent went to Australia. She had pictures of koalas and kangaroos and articles about the Great Barrier Reef posted to her twitter and Facebook accounts. He learned to scuba dive, tried to leave her in an underwater cave. She swam with the fish, no oxygen tank required. She left her dangling eyeball and some brain tissue for the fish, but the rest of her returned home with him.

He took her to the Louvre, Notre Dame before it burned, the d'Orsay in Paris, the Prado in Madrid, the Uffizi in Florence. "Don't get blood on the paintings," he told her, having given up hope she'd stay for the art.

When his savings were gone and couldn't afford another trip, he took her to a psychiatrist. "Doc, my friend is seeing dead people, well one dead person in particular." The shrink put Trent on antipsychotics. They made him sleepy and left Kara smiling permanently.

Trent took her to a psychic, admonishing himself for not thinking of it sooner. He told the psychic, "My friend won't move on. No matter what I do, she won't leave me alone." The woman came to his apartment. She burned sage and performed a ritual to open the door to elsewhere. When she finished, she packed up her things and said, "Your house has been cleansed. Your ghost is gone." Kara laughed so hard her jaw fell off.

Kara laughed even harder when Trent jumped from the bridge and woke up in the hospital. Once he was sufficiently recovered, they moved him to the locked ward on the third floor. She seemed to enjoy being there. The residents never minded the bits of skin she left lying around. He convinced the doctor to let him stay a little longer.

Then the unexpected happened on the third floor, behind the locked doors. For the first time, Trent saw him, that is to say, her ghost. He was rotting, leaving bits of his flesh behind as he followed her. Her second shadow. Her ghost's name was Roger and her name was Anne.

The doctor released Trent and Kara soon after he released Anne and Roger.

Every night, forever after, they had dinner together, she and her ghost, he and his ghost. And at night they slept together, Kara standing over her, Roger standing over him, their guilt standing watch together. 🍂

JOEY: THE MAGICAL AXOLOTL

JAMES RALEIGH

Joey, the magical axolotl, made me feel whole. While I lied down and cried, he comforted me. He spoke to me in John Lennon's voice with my father's words. Or, sometimes, he would speak in my father's voice with John Lennon's words. Meanwhile, Joey danced through the stuffy air, dripping golden flames from his tail in patterns that I had never seen. When I asked what they meant, he'd float silently in place.

The more I stared at Joey's fiery trails, the more the symbols started to make sense. Surely, they couldn't be gibberish. At first, I thought they might be Mexican characters from a time long ago, but wouldn't that be wrong? To assume their origin is Mexican just because he's an axolotl?

Then, I thought, perhaps the symbols were a code. I knew that computer code looks like 01011100 and biological code looks like AGGCAT, so it couldn't be either of those.

What could he be writing? I stared at Joey intently as we weaved and bobbed in front of the dark television. He opened his wide maw and said "Love is the flower you've got to let grow."

Before I knew it, there was another intricate golden inferno before me. I peered into it, stepping closer and closer. Was it cosmological? Did Joey know the language that had been used to write reality? As soon as I thought it, I knew it to be true. First, the television disappeared, and in its place sat a bowl of tomato soup. The pattern faded and Joey began writing anew. What would he eliminate next? What would he create?

The questions rushing through my head led to one conclusion. If Joey could rewrite reality with this code, others could learn to do it too. If anyone saw my magical axolotl friend writing as he did, they could bend the universe to their whim. Of course, they might not understand what the symbols mean. Even so, powerful men don't need to know the language to use a resource to their advantage.

My mind conjured images of Joey being tortured, manipulated, multiplied. A giant engine of flying salamanders rewriting the world's code. First they'd get rid of mosquitoes. That wouldn't be too bad. But it gets more complicated from there. Then, the engine starts producing diamonds from thin air, driving down their value and causing a financial crisis in Botswana. Once the Botswanians start rebelling, the powers that be will have no choice but to wipe them from existence. Joey's life essentially guaranteed a genocide.

I cried harder and harder, to which Joey said "Turn that frown upside down, kiddo."

The doorbell rang. Without another thought, I sprinted to the kitchen. I grabbed the steak knife and bolted back toward Joey. He seemed to be halfway done with his latest glyph. I plunged the cold blade into his amphibious heart, dragging him to the floor. I turned my attention to the incomplete symbol. It was now beginning to fade, and the rest of the world faded with it.

flash fiction

FISH BONE

LAUREN VILLA

I.   In the morning, Harold will sit down at his computer and pull up Google.

2.   He will type in a new search: is having a pet fish good for your heart?

3.   Harold will read about how watching fish swim is an odd but effective way to reduce stress and blood pressure.

4.   Harold's doctor, Dr. Riley, with her long black hair and chipped front tooth will tell Harold that he's in trouble.

5.   Harold will fantasize about what it would be like to spit in her mouth.

6.   Dr. Riley will, for no known reason, recall a time when she was at brunch with her girlfriends and the waiter convinced her that swallowing spit was sexy.

7. Dr. Riley will tell Harold that if he doesn't do something about his stress levels, he will need to start a new kind of medication.

8. It will be the kind that makes your skin flake off, she will say.

9. It will be the kind that makes your nightmares come to life, she will say to herself.

10. You're worrying me, Dr. Riley will tell Harold.

11. You need to do something about your health, Dr. Riley will say.

12. Then she will touch his leg.

13. Harold will go to Petsmart and turn down aisle 5.

14. He will ask a woman where the fish are and she will point to the end of the aisle and she will ask Harold if he has a napkin.

15. Only then will Harold realize that the woman's dog shit everywhere.

16. Harold will accidently step in shit.

17. Harold will run away to aisle 6 because cleaning up the shit could increase his stress levels.

18. Harold will scrape the bottom of his shoe on a bottom shelf with fish food.

19. Harold will see, and immediately, fall in love with a guppy.

20. He will name the guppy Priscilla.

21. He will ask the Petsmart woman in khaki pants how to take care of a guppy.

22. The Petsmart woman will recommend a large tank, a filter, plastic decorations, and blue rocks for the tank.

23. This will make a guppy thrive, she will say.

24. The Petsmart woman will back away from Harold because his breath smells like a dead crow.

25. Harold will put Priscilla, who is swimming around in a plastic bag, in his large, jacket

pocket and pay for the tank and the decorations and the rocks.

26. Harold will forget about Priscilla and forget to pay for her.

27. Harold will drive home and fall asleep on the couch.

28. Harold will wake up and realize that Priscilla is dead.

29. ·Priscilla will live her last moments gasping for air on top of Harold's dirty leather couch, underneath the weight of his chest.

30. In the morning, Harold will sit down at his computer and pull up Google.

31. He will type in a new search: how to save a dead fish?

32. He will take a thumbtack and pierce it through Priscilla's orange tail.

33. Her body will hang on the closet door next to his computer.

34. Her skin will grow more dry, flaking off and dropping into a mountain of dead scales on the floor below.

35. Everyday Harold will spritz her with water, although it won't do much.

36. He will fill up a little spray bottle that he will label with Sharpie, that says "Priscilla."

37. Dr. Riley will fall asleep wondering how Harold's heart is doing.

38. Harold will think he has work to do.

39. He will drive back to the Petsmart and buy another Priscilla.

40. He will put her in his pocket and walk out without paying.

41. He will pop the bag, pour the water into a cup and drink it while he watches her flop on the couch.

42. He will fall asleep on top of her.

43. In the morning he will take a thumb tack and put Priscilla #2 next to Priscilla #1.

44. He will make an appointment to see Dr. Riley.

45. Dr. Riley will wear her clean white shoes and wipe her hands with hand sanitizer before she listens to his heart.

46. Dr. Riley will smile even though the room smells like fish guts.

47. You're doing much better, she will say.

48. Harold will smile too, the bones in his jaw will move slow.

49. I got some fish, like you said I should, he will say.

50. Dr. Riley will nod her head.

51. Very good, she will say.

52. I got fifteen, Harold will say.

53. And his smile will harden, like a fish bone.

MENTAL

KATHARINA BEZUSHKO

Thermodynamic Psychology

Like the hourglass
I am entropic:
Sand spills from the top
And sinks to the bottom;
But spun upon my axis, then
All the grains fall down again.

Borderline

I can be capricious as the sea,
Under control of extrinsic powers
The current below, and the undertow,
And above the winds and showers.

Seeds of Focus

I stomp and trip through the garden
The air is hot; the flowers bright and sweet:
I water them, one at a time —
And often, I nurture the weeds as well
Because I cannot tell the difference.

Mania

I could run forever —
I could fly!
Transcend the earth below and touch the sky!

Hurtling through space, I am untethered —
And — I realize far too late — unfeathered —

Sinking

The surface is above me; I can see it.
I paddle upward, paddle upward, paddle upward . . .
And always, there is debris in my way . . .
I reach and comb and tear,
And am tangled and ensnared . . .
Hands bound, feet bound, heart bound . . .
Sinking . . .
The surface slips away
And I am drowned.

The summit is above me; I can see it
I climb upward, climb upward, climb upward . . .
And always, there are rocks in my way . . .
I chip and dodge and scale,
And am beaten and impaled
Arms broken, legs bloodied, heart battered. . .
Tumbling . . .
The summit falls away
And I am shattered.

I cannot swim, cannot climb, cannot rise . . .
I am always in my way.

Polarity

The earth
That nurtures and sustains us all
Spins and whirls in space —
Turning, changing, fluctuating
Gathering speed centripetally.
And like the earth,
I am bipolar and I spin —
If you find my cycles dizzying,
It is merely because
My axis is
So relatively small.

SHAKEN

KATHARINA BEZUSHKO

I love a bold and anxious thunderstorm;
Below his swelling clouds, this willow tree
Aroused, intrigued, inspired by his form —
He rumbles, low, invigorating me.
Bright dagger flashes, open up my core!
I stretch against the sky, and bid him, strike —
Oblivious to me who loves him more;
But he shocks pine and sycamore alike.
I cannot hold his torrents rushing through —
My boughs are whips that shudder in his gust;
Yet I do not expect the weather to
Reciprocate my yearning or my lust.
> When caprice brings the sun to roast my soul,
> His absence leaves me limp, but I am whole.

NUBIBUS FATUUS

KATHARINA BEZUSHKO

You laid me right there, on the undressed bed
Before the bare window, through which the light
Never seemed to change from dull winter grey
But the clouds, dark and dense, rolled and creeped and
Stretched into the room, like fingers of God —
And you, you hovered overhead, and smiled,
Exfoliating me, 'til I was raw
And real, and human, underneath it all
We rocked in rhythm, and it felt divine . . .

And I thought of my life, and my children
And how they'd fare were I suddenly gone —

And those curling, rolling, reaching fingers
Undulated through the sky
And the only words that slipped into my
Dizzy and elated mind were, "Don't stop —

"Fuck Me Until I Die."

And suddenly I could not breathe at all
You asked me if I needed a paper bag
For carbon dioxide and I said, no!
Because I was not a tree, but you thought
That was why people breathed into a bag —
Through tears, I broke into a wild-eyed smile,
I told you that was just a lie, and laughed,
And hyperventilated 'til I cried —
I've never felt so happy in my life.

HOW TO FORGET
THEIR NAME

COURTNEY HILDEN

At first, it will
seem to hold
fast
to you, like a bat
to night. You will drive

up the dark,
fooling yourself into believing
you can
chart its ombres. You will busy

yourself with other
tasks: prying

loose the ship's planks, boarding
up the windows, breaking down
the packages, taking
up that long-
wanted hobby of composing
aubades. One day, as you are

greeting
the dawn, the morning will
remind you
of them. You will ask yourself when

was the last
time. You will not recall
it was when you heard
a love song.

It may slip
            away
in parts—
the pronunciation, or the spelling, before

dissolving completely
like macaroni
necklaces. It may come back momentarily, in

parts: the syllable rhythm, its sense
it was poetry in another life. You will resolve

yourself to distraction: the aforementioned other
lovers, new names
for forgetting, fresh
partings, nocturne
serenades. Some

thing will finally rise
up out of the black
waters to grab

hold of you. With renewed

attention you will
admire how he picks
at his bones. With affection,
you will hold

his hands so the wounds
may heal. While out, one day,

as you and he lay waste
together, they will
approach

you. After the initial
greeting they will

wait.

For once, the silence
will love you, favour
        you
        instead. *Don't you*
remember
        me? You will tilt

your head to one
side. Unintentionally,

their portrait of you will begin
to melt like untempered
clay.

BETWEEN

JANE YOLEN

"Magic lies between things…"
Charles de Lint

There it is, that small caesurea
between lives, deaths.
That moment between breaths.

That spark arcing, two
electrodes, making light.
Night into day, day into night.

That month's turning,
spring into fall,
that quick-fire momentum, all

the magic in the world
we refuse to see.
Flash of understanding: you, me.

It's all there in the in between.

BABA YAGA AT THE BATH HOUSE

JANE YOLEN

So there she is, barely glimpsed
through the vapor curls,
taking her bath, washing away
the old magics.

Alone among the women,
their long dugs and crackling faces,
she laughs at their aches,
gnashes her iron teeth.

Says nothing about the weather,
the latest marriages, how many calves
were born without horns,
or girls become boys over the winter.

Instead she counts the minutes
till she can be back in her hut
without having to endure
more village gossip.

Where she can think about eternity,
the energy of maidens,
and the salty sweetness
of a naughty boy's flesh.

MYRDDIN IN THE WILDERNESS

JANE YOLEN

So far from home's soft comforts,
The silk linens, my woman
Who kept the bed warm
Even when my bones grew cold.
(Magic burns like ice through a mage.)

So far from cook's best meats,
I wander apple groves
Plucking out little green worms,
Flinging them into the air,
Hoping to see them fly.

I settle down on the emerald carpet
With only pigs for company,
Their skin surprisingly like my old nurse's.
Their grunts not at all conversation.
At least they do not complain.

I miss the fire in the hearth,
But spring has its compensations.
I long for chilled wine in my glass.
But winter ices the river
And the water tastes as sweet.

After long years here,
Seeking inspiration,
Being sometimes mad,
I am surprisingly at home:
Tussocks of grass my pillows,

Sky my painted ceiling,
A winding stair of rocks,
Pharmacy of herbs at my feet
And all the birds sing lullabies

When I sleep, when I wake.

MASKING / UNMASKING

JANE YOLEN

"Writing is both mask and unveiling"—E. B. White

It's a dance, of course, mask on, mask off,
a Balinese shadow play.

We follow the sway of hips, the touch of lips,
wallow in passions we don't ourselves have.

I would have whapped an actual Heathcliffe
with a frying pan had he touched my daughter.

Once I screamed in the theater at Phaedre's choices,
saying no good would come of it, but she didn't listen.

I'd have goaded Alice into insurrection,
overthrowing both Red and White queens.

And Oz was a monster, sending a child, a dog,
and three creatures to do his dirty work.

But who wears the mask?
Who does the unveiling?
Those are the question we forget to ask.

SOCRATES IN CAMOUFLAGE

JANE YOLEN

*". . .what keeps us from hearing a truth that it must come
to us camouflaged?" Christopher B. Nelson, President St John's College*

Socrates takes his camouflage coat
out of the virtual closet, green and black
like a summer's forest.

He puts on matching pants, hat
face mask, as if chlorophyll
is his natural element.

Out he goes to deliver what truths
the public needs, disguised
like a hunter after deer.

He drops the truths onto doorstoops,
mailboxes; love letters shoved
between window and sill.

Ever since then, the noble lie
has needed its camouflaged deliverer,
who never questions whether

We the People have the rigor
 or the knowledge to see it
unmasked, undisguised, real.

SKIN LIES

JANE YOLEN

"My skin lies."—Joan Lennon

You think you know me by my skin,
but it's a coat I don each day,
a fabrication, cover-up,
do not trust it any more
than you trust my clothes
to tell you the truth.

You think you know me by my smile,
but it's a mask I put on at will.
a mummery, camouflage,
do not trust it any more
than the fawn's spots
to tell tell you the truth.

You think you know me by my tales,
but they change every single day,
 a fiction, fabrication,
do not trust them any more
than the liar's brag
to tell you the truth.

You think you know me by my poems.
Perhaps, perhaps you do
if you read between the lines,
under the skin, past the smile,
beyond the tale, beneath the lie
where truth sits alone under the Bo

waiting to be found.

CAROL THE CAT KILLER

LINDA QUINLAN

hristine and I played hopscotch on most mornings in the summer. She loved to draw pictures inside the squares of beautiful stylish girls. Carol, the dreaded cat killer and girl torturer lived down the street from us and Christine and I were ever watchful, knowing that some time during our play she would show up. I thought I knew how to handle Carol, but Christine didn't. She wasn't used to seeing the small white and gray rabbits my father shot and dissected in the basement of our apartment or the deer he hung to dry on the tree in the backyard. I fished alongside him for years until one night I dreamt that the flounder we had caught had human eyes and cried as it thrashed against the metal sides of our boat.

This was 3rd grade, the year my grandmother moved into our cramped two bedroom apartment. She and I shared a double room and this was the first time I wasn't afraid of the dark or the dreaded dolls I'd stuffed into the L shaped closet in my room.

Every day at lunch I would sit with Christine and Louise. Louise's father was an undertaker and we loved to play vampire in the coffins. I would buy a Hoodsie Ice Cream cup and would mix until it was a smooth brown color. I put the ice cream into my mouth and imagine that I was poisoning Miss Cherry, our teacher that year, my brother and Carol the cat killer.

The chalk for hopscotch happened to be in Christine's hand the day Carol came to taunt us. Earlier that summer Carol had pushed me off the garage roof where I was sunning and left a huge bump on my head. Weeks passed before I could remember who I was. I didn't tell anyone what had happened; the story was I tripped and fell. I'd learned early in life that no one is a squealer and no one sees anything.

I saw how my father beat my brother because he was disappointed that my brother didn't fight back when the Zulo brothers picked on him. I didn't want my father to know that I hadn't fought back when Carol pushed me.

I didn't have time to say anything that hopscotch day. The evidence was flowing out of Christine's face. I stood there watching or I might have closed my eyes.

On that day in the middle of summer Carol had walked up to us and asked if she could play with us. I shrugged, but Christine ignored her request. I watched as Carol walked up to a neighbor's house. I really thought she was just going to ring the bell and run off leaving us to be yelled at by Mrs. Bass. Instead she picked up the empty milk bottle from the stoop and walked towards us. I backed up, but I don't think Christine saw her. I wanted to run but I couldn't leave Christine there on the sidewalk. Carol broke the bottle on the curb and Christine turned. I yelled out, but it was too late. Blood began to flow out of Christine's face as she fell to the ground and Carol pulled the bottle out of her face. Red was covering the white chalk and the pretty girls. Then Carol was gone.

An older neighbor girl was standing next to me now. Christine's mother seemed to come from nowhere and was screaming for help. I stood there, my head bobbing like an apple at Halloween.

Soon the summer was over and Christine never returned to school. My mother said that after her hospital stay her family moved away. Carol still lived down the street but after that took on a quiet form of torture in her back yard. I was hoping somebody would shoot her or send her to Danvers Mental Hospital where she could die like my grandfather, hands tied to a metal table.

A week after the incident as my father called it, he took me into the back yard and told me to stay put by the fence. When he returned he had a rifle in one hand and a watermelon in the other. He put the watermelon in front of the hanging deer tree and walked back to where I was standing. He told me Christine's face probably looked like a football, all sewed up and rubbery.

Slowly he put the rifle up against his shoulder and fired. I watched the watermelon explode into pieces, its juices spilling onto the grass. "This is what happens when you play with guns. Never touch my guns. Do you understand? Think of that melon as someone's head. Now you shoot."

short story

NIGHT LIFE

A. P. WEBER

he words croak out through dust in my throat, "Help me."

Across the table, the man is like a cold breeze. His voice laughs. "Help you, Joseph? After all I've already done for you?"

I lean. Lean over my coffee. Lean into my palm, wavering. "Please."

"Of course. Joseph. Of course. But for what?"

"Anything. Whatever you want."

He nods. Cool. Mr. Chill. "That's good. That's very good. I'm glad you came around. But I mean 'for what' in a more philosophical sense." He rephrases the question in a deliberate staccato: "What will you do with the life I save?'"

I blink at the gravel in my eyes. Shake my head.

Mr. Chill's lips go tight. "That's what I was afraid of. Do you even know what I gave you? I gave you a third more life. A third. Instead of sixteen hours in a day, you now have twenty-four. What are you going to do with a third more time on earth?"

I bat at the air by my face. Something's there. I can't see it but I can feel it. A spider web, maybe. "Whatever you want me to."

Chill catches my hand and places it like a live grenade on the table between us, his own hand atop it. "Listen to me. I can't help you if you don't help yourself."

He turns my hand palm up, leaves two tablets. White. The size of aspirin. But not aspirin.

"Take these," he says. "It won't solve anything, but you will feel better. In the morning you report to this address. You lost your job. I have one for you."

Mr. Chill writes on a napkin with the pen the waitress left.

"Don't be late," he says, rising and shrugging into his white, cotton blazer.

I watch the napkin and the pills in my hand. "What time?"

He's at the door now, ready to leave the diner. He doesn't turn around. "Morning."

And he's gone.

For a minute longer, I watch the gifts Mr. Chill left me. I swallow the pills and chase them with the ice water in the translucent plastic cup on the table. Then I crumple the napkin into my coat pocket.

I want to fall asleep right there in the diner. I don't. In two minutes, I feel better.

I first met Mr. Chill a few days ago. Three, four, Five? Not sure how many. I haven't slept since.

I had a job. But I lost it. I've been losing a number of things as of late--sleep being the foremost on my mind. How did I get here? All I know for sure is that it all starts with Kelly Burbank.

Ms. Burbank is the kind of girl who makes you ashamed to be the man you are. I would talk to her sometimes. She'd be the only other person in the building most nights. Usually she'd say nothing, just hand me the wastebasket from under her desk.

Once, I said something like, "Burning the midnight oil, huh?" And she smiled. I couldn't tell if it was a polite or an embarrassed smile. Was she embarrassed by my presumption or the clumsy cliche? I thought about that a lot.

Another time, I asked her about her books. She said she was studying journalism. I told her about this program on public radio. She knew the one I was talking about, said she applied for an internship there, but didn't get it. Instead, she works here at the publishing house, goes to class during the day, and they let her stay late to finish her work. Mostly editing. She told me all this, looking over her shoulder without turning her body toward me.

After our first real conversation, I started working out. Push-ups in my living room. Pull-ups in my bathroom door jam.

I asked her, one night, if she ever sleeps.

"Nope," she said. "Don't have time."

I knew that meant she didn't want to talk either, so I left her alone. I didn't bother her for the rest of the week. On the following Monday, she came into the break room for coffee while I was cleaning the fridge. She leaned against the kitchen counter with her mug in both hands and said: "So what's your story?"

"No story," I said.

"Someone once told me: 'people with shitty jobs are making the most interesting art.'"

"This job isn't that bad."

I met Mr. Chill a couple days later. I went to the diner down the street from the building I clean. I do that sometimes after work--sit, drink coffee, watch the world wake up around me. Chill came in like a regular and sat down across from me. I'd never seen him before in my life.

Cool Mr. Chill. He's easy. Easy to talk to. Easy to listen to. Make eye contact with. Trust.

I told him my story. The real reason I'm where I'm at--the truth I'd never tell pretty Ms. Kelly Burbank. I didn't do a good job telling it; but Chill put all the pieces together, gave it pith.

"So you needed more time. Weren't ready to start a family and she was."

"Something like that."

"When did this happen?"

"We signed the papers almost six months ago."

"Time goes by so fast."

"Yeah."

"Think of how much of it we waste. If you could do more in a day, wouldn't that solve every-thing? If you had more time, you could have a family and everything else you want out of life. You wouldn't have to choose."

"Yeah. But where do I get more time?"

"Stop sleeping."

I laughed. But he was serious.

What happened next is a blurry jumble. I went somewhere with him, but the rest of my memories of that night are swirling light trails burnt into my retina. I can hear Chill's easy voice saying, "Just relax, this will only take a moment."

Then I was at home.

I laid awake in the half light of my apartment. I couldn't think of anything else to do, so I just laid there. I got up when I normally would, did some push-ups, ate some breakfast, went to work.

He didn't tell me I would feel so tired.

"Long night?" Kelly asked, handing her wastebasket over.

"Yeah. I guess so."

"You need to wake up."

"You're telling me."

I went to the diner after work. Chill didn't show; he had said he might.

At home I tried to do more push-ups, but my muscles were sore. I sat on the couch and watched TV. Kept getting this feeling like an hour or two had passed in the space of a single commercial. I'd blink and it would be the same cat scratching at the litter box, animated odor waves rising from the sand. That's all it was, a blink. But, God, it seemed so long.

Outside, traffic waxed and waned. People went to their jobs. Children went to school. They all came home again.

God I was tired.

At work, hours passed in geological time. During a single foot fall, I dreamed I was an astronaut trapped in a space capsule with no windows or doors. I floated weightless for hours until the impact of my foot against the linoleum roused me. The void still hummed outside the capsule until I turned the vacuum off.

I took my lunch break early, went to the diner and sat in a booth.

Eventually, Chill arrived and sat down across from me. "You don't look good."

"I'm tired."

"That's what happens when you don't sleep."

"Why did you do this?"

"You know why. To help you. To give you more time to get your life on track."

"I can't—"

"Yes. There are side effects. But I can help you with those. We can help each other."

I blinked and for the first time saw him as he truly was. Radiant, beautiful, an angel of light.

"Do you know what I do?" he said, and his brilliant aura disappeared. "We talked about you last time, I never got a chance to tell you about me. It's okay. But now it's my turn to talk. About me."

I rubbed grains of sand into my eyes and tried to open them wider. He went on talking.

"What I do is help people. Not just people like you who need a little bit of a push to get their lives on track. I also help other people. Wealthy people. Sometimes they have complicated problems. Tricky, delicate situations. Sometimes, simple problems. They want something. For example, there's this box, discovered in a shipwreck at the bottom of the Adriatic. It dates back to the Byzantine empire, the only one of its kind left in the world. And it can calculate the position of the stars with unimaginable precision. Have you heard of this?"

I nod. "Discovery Channel, I think."

"My mind reels at the implications of such an invention. I think about it all the time. Can you imagine? A man, just a simple man, without the aid of computers—not even a calculator—built this device. And it still functions today. I think, 'What have I done that compares?' It makes me want to use every second I have to the very best of my ability. Because a second is infinite, really. Infinite potential. But then—and this is what really bends my noodle—when you think about the very cosmos the box represents, you realize what a lark the last thousand or so years are since that box was built. No one remembers the man who built it. He's dead anyway, and the box is just a toy to be sold on the black market. Do you get what I'm saying?"

I was starting to.

"Right now," he went on, "this priceless piece of antiquity is on public display at the Museum of Science and Industry. My client wants it on the private market. See? Simple problem."

Then Mr. Chill leaned across the table. "But how are we going to get it for him?"

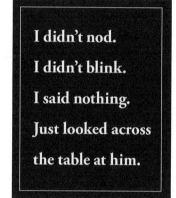

I didn't nod.
I didn't blink.
I said nothing.
Just looked across
the table at him.

I took it for a rhetorical question, but Chill just stayed there, inclining toward me as if he expected an answer.

Finally, I said, "I don't know."

Chill pulled back, threw his arms over the back of the booth.

"Well you should think about it. Because how you answer that question will determine whether I will continue to help you."

"I don't want your help anymore, I just want to get some sleep."

Mr. Chill sighed. "No, you do not need to sleep. You need to wake up."

"No. No. I need to sleep."

"Technically, you can still sleep. For very, very short periods. Seconds at most. Not enough to keep you sane. Do you know what will happen to you?"

I didn't nod. I didn't blink. I said nothing. Just looked across the table at him.

"You will, very quickly, begin to lose your mind. You will dream and not know it. Waking dreams that will come in waves. Your brain won't be able to write new memories properly. Your metabolism will stop functioning properly. Your immune system will shut down. You will be a raving mad, human husk in a week, tops, living out a torturous hell as you die."

I said, "go fuck yourself."

I didn't go back to work right away. I wandered around downtown, went to a bar, got drunk, threw up.

The night was warm. I took my shoes off and I could feel the concrete vibrating against the soles of my feet. Living energy. The essence of the city. The aggregate heartbeats of every sleeping person in every building connected by this asphalt grid. This nervous system.

I blinked and it was gone, so I went back to work.

Maybe Mr. Chill was lying. Maybe I would fall asleep eventually. When that happened, when I got back to normal, I would need my job. At least, that's what I thought at the time. Dawn was approaching. The professionals would be returning to smudge the glass and fill their trash cans and piss on the floor in front of the urinals. I had to hurry.

That's when I heard the voices of children playing in the empty halls, always around a corner, or behind a door. And when I'd turn my back they'd be right behind me, shrill and shrieking. I chased the voices until I found them outside the sixth floor window. I pounded on the glass, trying to find a window that would open.

Kelly found me. I didn't know she was still there.

She smiled the kindest smile I had ever seen. Not shy. Not embarrassed. Kind. I remember crumbling in a corner of the room and asking her if she could hear the children too.

She bent down and held my chin in her hand. She said, "I can't believe you told him to go fuck himself."

An ice age thawed every time I blinked my eyes. When the paramedics got there they asked where the 'EDP' was. I guess they meant me. They put a needle in my arm and everything got worse. The blinks came more quickly. I dreamed with each blink, and each dream evaporated like a forgotten aeon.

It went on and on—the prophesied hell Chill spoke of.

Until it got better.

I recall a flash and the hallucinations were gone, washed away in a tsunami of consciousness. The surface of my brain was covered in fresh, new, pink skin; it made my scalp tingle.

It felt so good.

"You need to get out of here."

White sheets. A curtain. Linoleum. Fluorescent lights. An emergency room, I reasoned. Kelly leaned over me, her hands on both sides of my face, forcing my head to turn and look up at her.

"I gave you a little bit of a treatment. Not a full one, because it's one of my own and I need it. I would have given it to you back at the office, but my boss got there early and called 9-1-1. So get up and get out of here before they throw you in the State Hospital or whatever they do with junkies and crazy people."

"What's going on?"

She drew the IV needle from my arm without ceremony; the tube ran to a syringe in her hand. She disconnected the syringe and stuffed it into her pocket. "Get up!"

She pulled me to my feet, pressed my wallet into my hands. "Here. Let's go."

"Where did you get this?"

"Let's go."

And we left. Right out the sliding glass doors. No one seemed to notice.

In front of the hospital she said, "I don't think anyone ever turned him down before. I can respect that you did. But you'll die if you don't do what he wants. Go find him. Make a deal."

And she walked away--just as Beth pulled up.

Beth leaned into the passenger seat of her sedan and called to me through the open window, "Joey!"

"Beth? What are you doing here?"

I looked around for Kelly. She was gone.

"What are you looking for?" Beth said. "Are you hurt or something?"

"I'm fine," I said and opened the passenger door. "What are you doing here?"

She made a face I knew, like we were married again, and she wasn't happy about it.

"Nice to see you, too. Do me a favor and change your emergency contact information."

"They called you?"

"Honestly, Joey, who else would they call? What happened? Are you okay?"

"I think so. No, yes. I feel great."

She looked at me, studied my face. "Get in the car. I'll give you a ride."

She pulled up to my place. We sat, the car idling.

I reached for the door, then stopped. "I was thinking. I know you're with what's his name. I'm not trying to horn in on that. I just—when we were married, it felt like there was always something around the corner, something more I couldn't get my hands on. I wanted... more. And I didn't want to settle down, have kids, buy a house—because I thought, you know, what if? Maybe you felt like, I don't know, you weren't enough for me. But it wasn't that at all. You were the best thing in my life, and I'm sorry. I'm sorry I let it all get so screwed up. It wasn't you. It was me. It was all my fault."

She was looking at her hands, limp on the bottom of the steering wheel.

"I know you see it that way," she said; she looked over at me like I were a very sick child. "But you're wrong. That's not why I left you, anyway. Look. I loved you. I still love you. But you are not the man I want to be married to. I want the house, I want the kids, I want the life. I want all that. I don't want you. You... don't work with all that. What I'm saying is: it's not that you want too much. You don't want enough."

This was a conversation we'd never had before.

In the absence of my reply, she shrugged and said, "Or you don't want anything bad enough. I don't know. Either way..."

I took a breath and opened the door.

"You've given me something to think about," I said, dumbly. "I have a lot more time on my hands now, so, that's good, I guess."

She touched my leg. "Please... Please take care of yourself, Joey."

I put my hand on hers. "Thanks for the ride."

I was fired from my job, so, instead of going to work that night, I went to the diner and waited. I drank coffee and tipped the waitress over and over again, all night and into the next morning. I walked around town and came back. Ordered breakfast. Waited. Beer. Coffee. Waited and waited. At some point, whatever Kelly gave me began to wear off. That day became another. In the diner. Around town. Back again. The waitress seemed nonplussed by my behavior, like she'd seen it all before—the actions of some lame Sisyphus pushing his coffee cup to the edge of the table.

Finally, a breeze blew in from the door, and there he was. Mr. Chill. He walked over to my table. With every other step he took, I blinked one of my eternal blinks. He sat down, and I begged him to give me another chance. "Help me," I said. That's when he gave me the pills and the address and made an appointment with me for "Morning."

> With every other step he took, I blinked one of my eternal blinks. He sat down, and I begged him to give me another chance.

The address Chill gave me is to a brick townhouse. The hills in Northwest, a nice neighborhood with lots of iron gates and stone and ivy.

It's after seven a.m. when I arrive. A man with eye sockets like plums answers the door. He wears an expensive-looking suit that seems especially tailored for his wiry frame. The tip of a tattoo on his neck peeks out from behind his collar. He looks me over and pops his knuckles one by one--a green, tattoo-ink letter on each finger: 'N-I-T-E' and 'L-I-F-E.' He steps aside and jerks his head toward the interior of the house. I go in. Knuckles puts his fist in his palm like it's his at-ease stance and nods in the direction of the stairs. I climb to the sound of his cracking joints behind me.

At the top of the stairs, a doorway opens into an office. The decor is sparse. On one wall is a print of Goya's Saturn Devouring His Son, and on the wall across from it is another painting I do not recognize depicting the same scene from the myth. A vague sense of apprehension tightens inside my chest.

Mr. Chill stands behind a dark and shiny wood desk in the center of the room. He's facing the window, looking out at the dew-slick morning streets.

"It's been morning for over seven hours, Joseph. I do not normally tolerate this kind of ineptitude."

Chill turns around and smiles a forgiving smile.

"Consider this your warning," he says.

I nod and look at the floor.

Chill sits down in the plush high-back chair behind his desk and watches me for several seconds. "Did you bring a resume?"

I shake my head.

His face is a facade of exaggerated disappointment. "What kinds of skills do you have?"

I shrug my shoulders. "I'm a janitor."

"Do you have a high school diploma?"

"I went to OSU."

"Oh?" Chill raises his eyebrows—a mockery of flattery. "What did you major in? Sanitary engineering?"

"Literature."

"Mm. That explains it."

He looks me over like he's taking measurements for a suit--or a coffin.

I clear my throat. "What were those pills you gave me?"

"You want more?"

I look at Chill, right in the eyes. I can't tell if he's really offering them to me, mocking me or doing something else entirely. I decide to say nothing.

"You're scared. I can see it. Good. I'm giving you another chance, Joseph. How long has it been since you last slept—since I gave you this gift? Have the hallucinations started yet?"

He waves away his own questions. "The pills were just a quick fix. What you really need is a treatment. A treatment will take care of all the side effects of sleeplessness—for a little while, anyway. But you are going to have to work for it. Every time, you're going to have to prove you deserve it. You said 'no' to me once. You don't get to say it again. Do you understand?"

I nod.

"Good."

Chill takes a set of keys out of the desk drawer, sets them down and slides them over.

"Now, I can see you're a coward. So I'm not going to ask anything too taxing of you for now."

I pick up the keys and look at them.

"You'll be my driver," Chill says. "I expect you here at twelve a.m. everyday. You don't get paid. You're done when I tell you you're done. You get your treatments exactly as often as I deem it necessary for you to receive them. Understand?"

"How—"

"Do you understand?"

"Yes, but how—"

"That is not my problem. Be here at twelve a.m. everyday, and you do everything I ask. That's it. The day you don't show—the day you tell me 'no'—you're done. You get one warning about this shit. Do. You. Understand?"

I nod.

"Say it."

"I understand."

"Good."

I hear Knuckles behind me. Pop. Pop. Pop. Chill nods at him.

"The kid's here," says Knuckles.

At the bottom of the stairs is a boy, maybe seventeen. He's tall, handsome. He has a book bag on his shoulder. When he sees Chill he looks nervous the way teenagers do.

"There he is!" Chill says with sudden exuberance. "Have you had breakfast yet? I know a place."

I drive them to that diner. On the way, Chill asks the kid questions, tells him interesting stories. By the time they get out of the car, the kid isn't awkward anymore.

I go park and wait. I wonder what they're talking about in the diner. But it doesn't matter what—I know where it's going. The kid has a problem. A sick mother. Hospital bills stacking up. No money for college. And he has a dream. He needs more time—all day and all night—to fix his problems or to make his dream come true. Chill can 'help' him with that. The kid will love him—probably already does. But Chill hasn't started squeezing him yet.

After breakfast, I drive them to Grant High School; it's where I used to go--a long time ago, now, long before time started killing me. The kid gets out.

"I'll see you tomorrow night, Kevin," says Mr. Chill, and pats the back of my seat to go.

Through the mirror, I watch the kid walk across the grass toward the big, brick building, and I can't shake the sense that I've abandoned him to die.

"I have a job for you," says Chill as I drive.

I glance at him in the rearview mirror and say nothing.

"That girl. The one who helped you. I'm done with her."

I just keep driving.

When we get to the townhouse, I park and turn around in my seat. This will be the second time I've had to beg him.

"I'll do anything, man. I'll steal that box. Whatever you want. But I can't—I can't hurt that girl."

Chill holds up his hand. "Are you saying 'no?'"

"I'm saying, 'please.' I'm saying, 'I'll do the box job.' I'll do anything."

He nods, licks his lips. "You are so pathetic. You know that's why she picked you, right? And just to spite me. I asked her to find me a real player. Instead, she brings me you. The box job is off the table. You want a treatment, you do what I say. I can't have two of you piece-of-shits undermining my operation."

"Please."

"It's you or her. One of you gets the treatments, the other dies. If you're merciful, you will put a bullet between her eyes. Or you can drown her in mop water. Whatever a low-life janitor does to commit murder. But do it tonight."

I still have my keys from my old job. I find her in the breakroom, pouring coffee. She looks up at me, then drops her eyes to my hand--the fat, black .45-caliber Glock I hold against my thigh. She nods at the gun.

"Did he give you that?"

I blink and look away.

"He told you to kill me," she says.

It's not a question—she knows.

We stand there for a beat longer. I think about raising the gun. My hand twitches, but that's all I can manage. She takes a sip of her coffee.

"He knows you won't do it. He knows you can't. He knows everything, even if he pretends he doesn't. It's this game he's playing--to toy with me. You don't even matter."

Finally, I lift my eyes to her; they feel rusty. My head aches. I'm so goddamn tired. "What--what do you mean?"

"He knows you're not going to do it. He just wants me to know I fucked up. That I'm on his shit-list, or whatever. So I'll toe the line."

She takes another sip of her coffee. "You should have done a better job of begging. You should have impressed him. What did you do, tell him to fuck off again? Whatever it was, he's going to make you suffer now."

My legs feel weak. There's a chair beside me and I slump into it. My hand falls on the table; the gun rests on its surface, inert. I couldn't pick it up again if I tried. "What do I do?"

Kelly sets her coffee on the table across from the pistol. Her voice is soft and small and she says, "You kill me."

Her eyes are glossy.

"I'm done," she says in the same small voice. "I can't do this anymore. I'm done."

She sits down across from me, clears her throat.

"Listen. It's the only thing that makes sense. He thinks he can control us. But if you do it, if you actually kill me--that's a freewill choice. It's the only real choice you have."

Her voice is small again.

"Please do it."

Then confident.

"I want you to do it."

I rub my temples. How much time do I have before the pills Chill gave me in the diner wear off completely? How much time until I lose my mind again. My stomach hurts. Every second matters now.

I push my chair back, stand and grip the Glock. She closes her eyes; crystal beads stream down her cheeks. For an infinite second, the teardrops hang at her chin, and I am trapped inside each. Trapped in thought. It's just a second, but it tells me what to do.

"There's a kid," I say. "A high school student—Grant High School. His name's Kevin."

Kelly opens her eyes and looks at me. I'm holding the gun at my side.

"He's next," I tell her. "He's going to do to Kevin what he did to us. Tomorrow night. He's going to do it."

I can see in her eyes that she knows exactly what I'm talking about. I can see her making her own choice.

I put the gun down on the table.

"His name's Kevin," I tell her again. "I don't know how much time I have left before I lose it again. Not long, I guess. It's okay. I've earned my death now. But you still have to earn yours. Remember, his name is Kevin."

I know I'm rambling, but she nods like she gets it, so I leave.

My mind unravels as I walk. I can't shake the sense that someone awaits me outside. So I walk like I have an appointment. A rendezvous with a stranger everyone knows.

I go to meet him.

In the dark. ♥

AFTERMATH

C. KUBASTA

My father told me to
turn the lights on when the sky
got soft & greenish grey – after the F-scale winds, when
people might be picking their way
through the wreckage of what was home, and ours
untouched

we had a roof, food, electricity

Come spring, we'd clean the mice
out of the bucket of used motor oil
in the garage, silken lumps fished out of a skein
of treacle. Used motor oil has many uses, beyond
a death-trap for unlikely families, in an unlikely place.

We are talking about fathers because both your father
and stepfather had told you *You can't trust anyone*
who bleeds five days & doesn't die –

Now, when there's a storm, I still think we should get the chainsaw
and walk around to the neighbors, cutting
brush, clearing what needs clearing, checking
in. I recognized that lumpen death

smothered in the grey-green of dirty oil
because earlier that year I'd found a nest
in the cap on the propane tank:
pink & hairless, I put them back
before anyone else saw. Viscous-slick,
they'd been tempered to the ultimate vulnerability.

I want to tell you

how down the hill, by the creek, there were these plants
we called Touch-Me-Nots – some kind of jewelweed, with orange flowers
and sweet nectar, and we'd rub it on broken or itchy skin, but
mostly we liked to poke the cylindrical pods, watch them split & furl back
onto themselves. In the moted light, we could watch the trajectory
of the seeds. You are surprised I've never heard that saying, but what I learned

is how to manage lumpen death, a chainsaw, and to touch
everything that claims to not want touch.

CARDINAL DIRECTIONS

C. KUBASTA

Trying to bring contraband home, we pack the checked luggage,
send it with the grandparents. Some shells, a piece of brain coral, but
it gets pulled in the screening. I have something small

in my carry-on. I've had luck with small transgressions, little
souvenirs. Once I brought back a turtle shell wrapped in dirty panties
and even though it triggered a bad check, the screener stopped, reluctant
to work his way through. Maybe I've just been lucky – maybe. Still,
I think the way to hide something precious or prohibited
is to wrap it in something more so.

The woman taking orders for coffee at the gate had a bleeding mouth
and she kept licking the new red, or wiping her lip with her sleeve
and looking, checking to see if & how it was healing. Maybe
a split lip from some innocuous event – maybe.

A translated line from Akhmatova reads, "We have learned that
blood smells only of blood" and maybe – maybe, but there's also

taste, and this sends me down a rabbit hole to childhood:

each wound within reach of the early antiseptic of ourselves,
each jagged-toothed cut from a fall on asphalt stippled the sweet red insides
of the mouth, tasting that as we run to catch up, brush ourselves off, keep
going, after friends or siblings or cousins or whatever

we were chasing. I remember a curtain-darkened room mid-day – his voice
saying "iron-filings," my limbs stretched toward the cardinal directions
of box spring corners. But I don't recall if that was in reference to smell
or taste. I recall relief in that moment. But we were in childhood

a moment ago, and I've ruined it. Akhmotova wasn't writing about childhood either, although she began with the smells of wild honey & a girl's mouth.

Maybe childhood ends when we learn to hide the precious thing. Maybe
our own blood smells only of blood. The precious thing

has different names, and some of them may be dirty. Someone – maybe –
will be afraid to touch it; someone – maybe – will uncover it. What matters

is the curtain-dark room, and whether one of you will name it:
childhood is over when we know blood other than our own.

POGROMS AND SHOAHS

S. PRESTON DUNCAN

The old men were tying tzitzit around
the edges of evening.

I remember them smiling
in the gunmetal gray
of mumbled prayer
as though holding something
serrated
between their teeth.

That's how we
were taught to pray -
like we were lacing up the boots
of dead men

learning to laugh.

AGKISTRODON CONTORTRIX

S. PRESTON DUNCAN

In the afternoon
I killed
a copperhead.

young
female
full of
potential.

She was just there
like in the dream
beneath a shadow
something heavy
    balanced
    on her back.

Her skin was gorgeous
    as an omen.

I broke a cinder block
    over her head.

While I skinned it
    I was sure
it would come back
    to bite me.

        Later
    at the gallery
the walls were full of snakes.

A woman I knew
danced on a

stage
taking up serpents
smashing apples.

Their flesh was an allergy of glitter
like a cheap secret
that just spreads
after the skin
breaks

they sounded like bricks
in the garden

she was aching with new tattoos

my hands were drowning when
I buried her head in the yard,
covered myself in smoke

some things you can't wash off

CROW

JACKIE SHERBOW

Sometimes I think I'd
say anything. Sometimes I ask
for silence in small thoughts
like rosary beads, counting
one two three four five six
Even my own body
would thank me, my vocal
cords covered in knots,
my day-after brain, and
that dark, oily bird.

The accusers
in Salem saw birds everywhere:
in the meeting-house
in the woods
human women turning to birds
human women and sometimes
men holding birds, yellow birds
controlling them. Mine
is uncontrollable,
even with awareness of it
pressing itself against the inside
of my body where at least
I can keep it warm.

GOLDFINCH

JACKIE SHERBOW

Washing the dishes I received
three cuts on my right
index finger: scratches
from a small sharp claw.
I'd been thinking about how the joke
I overheard on the subway wasn't
really a joke, how I could only hear
the girl's side of the conversation,
how she was angry.

At a certain temperature, wounds
reopen—literally:
the cut on my finger
becomes pink and soft,
a square of skin made   different.
The floor is dirty
and the bottoms of my feet
track the dirt along with me.
Looking at my marked body
I can see why the girls
blamed other bodies—
I don't have their hunger
or their puritanism
or the unabashed
New England winter
and still I want to blame   you.

I'm noticing: the spots
appearing on both of us;
my heart rate rising;
bugs in the lamp globe.
Hysteria   or a yellow bird
in my teeth   or a yellow

bird   a yellow bird
and what our neighbors
would say to see
our dirty dirty floor.

FAMILIAR

JACKIE SHERBOW

Your claws were sharper than
I'd expected, but your beak
was small and pale—almost
delicate. Your call was
quiet but insistent.
Outside was the most
constant thunder I'd ever
heard. You woke me up
and I worried for you,
out in the storm.
The rain slicked off
your oily wings.
you found shelter
in my bedside table.
I wanted you to leave.
In the morning, the air
had turned blue and you
had turned into a stomach ache
flying by me as I walked,
at waist level. You're always
in orbit around me; I can predict
your path. I break into a jog
to shake you.

THE WIZARD'S LAST ADDRESS

JACKIE SHERBOW

We went to hear it, and it felt like we
would die soon, too, like our last show: the smell of peanuts, gas
and flame, the blown-glass animals, and real ones: hooves, slick manes,
the thing I'd feared, had always feared, had dreamed about and sang
of in my sleep had come: the very last of all the chance
I'd ever have, and it was full of salt, of songs, of you,
of me, of me. I saw I'd been a knight of errant tasks,
forgetting touch and taste and breath, my hands like probes to find
the far-off stuff, but never winning favor, magic lost
while questing, turned to oil, steam, and metal, broken down
to basest distillations, seeping back into the lake.

PROPHECY

JACKIE SHERBOW

Yesterday, I read that Merlin's
father was a demon. I had been trying
again to escape and there he was:
waiting for me down
a deep-blue hallway

It was all clear last night, prophet
that I am, I was all of it:
A foaming beer with bright
cake sprinkles inside; my mother,
looking at me with hatred;
a pair of globe-eyes, pupils
contracting and dilating; Instagram
posts with rainbow filters;
someone I didn't know,
but know now; an Arctic hare
my lover finds, bridles,
and brings home
under the arm, in armor
made of rain.

The king's soldiers wanted
Merlin, who couldn't be had.
The animals' claws are sharp,
but I am the one
who can point them.

TO ENVY A SNOWFLAKE

SEAN WILLIAM DEVER

I watch the snowflakes come to life.

They dance their descent,
I envy every falling one.

Destined to die by heat, warmth –
yet free of disease.

They fall to the ground
in perfect order,
determined before their fall.

Cling together –

aware that innate unison
is self-destructive in itself.

I pull myself from the window
overlooking the freshly-dusted city street,
retreating,
back to the warm confines of bed.

Freshly cleaned linens scratch
my chest and upper thighs,
pale white sheets meet my neck.

Leaning forward,
I thought I heard the ringing of my phone,
but when I looked,
no one had called.

Continuing to lay in bed
looking, absent-mindedly at the ceiling

recalling a time in which
there was someone to call.

Self-loathing –
not a tune I wished to play
least, so consciously.
I think again of the snowflakes –
absent of choice,
free of sickness.

MANNEQUIN FOR HIRE

SEAN WILLIAM DEVER

Place me in a storefront window
on Newbury St. preferably, All Saints,

but leave me naked.
Let my pod and CGM drape

under the spotlights
for the passersby to gawk,

pause, and photograph the flaws
chiseled on the backs of my arms,

stomach, and thighs. Where
scar tissue and bruises

rule my skin,
where insulin rashes

turn to insulin scars.
Prop me so my right arm extends,

the holes in my fingers greet those
who dare to window-shop close enough

see small caverns of darkness
and dried blood, face to face

with the mortality that capitalism
sweeps away, as bodies pile

upon one another
in front of CVS and Walgreens.

Vials of Novolog $289 (up $200
from eight years ago)

while the screeches
of garbage trucks removing

the diseased from your eyes,
eyes trained by the government.

When the season changes
and this look is outdated,
tuck me in the basement,
among other trends of past years,

place issues of *The New York Times*
at my feet, issues that illuminate

the growing number of deaths per year
of those without enough insulin

to keep ketoacidosis from poisoning
their blood in days, or hours – dust me

when time begins to show and nerves
further purple my feet.

Change my pod every three days
or throw out my PDM

so the repeated alarms don't
interrupt your day.

But whatever you choose,
leave me naked.

A Good Witch's Guide to Teach and Learn Death

BEKKIE JEAN MURPHY

ption No. 1

Find the wren carcass on your front porch, and if the body has been there fewer than two days, acquire a pint of goat's blood from your neighbor (either call upon on an earthly favor to which he is indebted or place a honey jar spell under their deck). Sift three handfuls of sand from your children's sandbox. Paint a pentagram around the wren's stiff body and throw sand at it while whispering, "Tabula Rasa Per Capitar Non Sequitir!" Be quiet as to assure your neighbors do not discover you are a family of witches. Leave lifeless body and wait for it to wake up.

Option No. 2

Give the carcass CPR for five minutes. Use a straw as to not contract a virus. Place the pad of your finger over its chest and tap lightly. Picture your life force channeling into the body with each gentle tap. The wren is small, so it will only require the life force in your two pointer fingers. Give up. You broke all its bones and it was dead anyways.

Option No. 3

Let the carcass sit on the porch and rot, but bring the baby birds inside. When the maggots come, collect them and feed to the babies. Try to keep the nestlings warm so they won't die. String together daisies and cloves to raise vibration in their spirits.

Option No. 4

Pick up the dead wren carcass, wrap it up in an old newspaper, and bury it in the backyard. Dig the hole at least six inches deep and pack it down so no animals can get to it. If there are bobcats or coyotes in your backyard, cover the grave in black pepper. It will deter the animals from digging it up. Put the pepper in the form of a cross to ward off evil spirits.

Option No. 5

Tell your son to do Solution No. 4. Tell him it'll put hair on his chest, and all warlock's require hairy chests (see *Raising a Proper Warlock*, Chapter 7).

Option No. 6

Tell your daughter to do Solution No 4. Tell her to defy stereotypes. Good witches defy stereotypes and overcome obstacles without crying (see Raising a Proper Witch, Chapter 5).

Option No. 7

Use the bird as an opportunity to teach your young witch and warlock about the fragility of life. Tell them sometimes bad things happen to good creatures and we don't know why. Tell them not to be mad. You were never a good witch anyways.

short story

SKELETON KEY

EVELYN DESHANE

T he last time I heard from Sally was in the ER the night I broke my wrist. We spent two hours waiting before a doctor saw me. Then, when my sex marker (F) didn't match how I currently looked (M) or my name (Ryan), it was another two hours before the doctor came back with x-rays.

Sally made a jerk off motion behind the doctor's back when he left for the second time and refused to meet our eyes. When we were alone, she made the jerk-off motion to me, too.

"I bet that's how you broke it. Too aggressive with your sex toys. I know you're all about sex positivity, but you positively snapped that wrist."

I laughed. Sally and I were quite the pair. I looked like a twelve year old boy before the testosterone shots made my chin sprout fuzz and my body bulk out. Her hormones made her face heart-shaped and gave her breasts. She was thirty-seven, but still dressing like she was in tenth grade and wanted to get the footballer's attention.

I couldn't blame her. I had broken my wrist trying to impress the local jock at my gym, only to slam backwards and snap against a wall.

"You know, you're right," I told her. "I was jerking off when I broke this."

"Told ya."

I already knew the procedure for broken bones in the Ontario ER system. After my x-rays, I was supposed to get a cast, but at this rate, I'd be there all night.

"You don't have to stay, you know," I told Sally. "Thanks for driving me, but I know you have a date."

"I do. A pretty date."

"The guy with the red car again?"

"And the scar on his chin. The scar and the car," she said and laughed. She was dressed in two inch heels and a pink top that matched the highlight of her eyes. When I'd met her in group, she said pink was her favourite colour. No one let her say that before she was thirty five, so she was catching up for lost time. Her nails glittered as she went through the file the doctor left in my stall. She held up my x-ray towards the light, her nails still shimmering.

"Goddamn. It looks like you fractured this."

"Nope. Just a lot of little breaks," I repeated the doctor's words. "One of the most common injuries in adults. Not a big deal."

"Yeah, but if you're not careful, your bones will be all you have. So you gotta take care of 'em. That's why you always gotta be on hormones. If you ever get your uterus out, you know to take them forever and ever, yeah? Don't be like me. Don't cut your balls and run."

I didn't laugh at her joke this time. Her harsh lesson in biology had been her follow up to her favourite colour story in group. She'd gotten an orchiectomy, thinking it was the smart way to rid her body of testosterone. As it turned out, hormones are good for bone growth. And not just menopausal women break their hips. Sally had shattered her hip pelvis when she was thirty-four, three years after removing her nuts without actually transitioning. So when everything was all repaired, metal holding her skeleton together, she figured it was better late than never to start liking the colour pink.

"And if, you know, God Forbid we ever die," she added, her tone just the same as when she asked if I had jerked myself off into this broken wrist, "our bones are gonna be the only things that identify us. So always make sure to check with your dentist. Change your name there first. And everything else, well, die in the proper clothing. And hope to God gender doesn't' exist in the goddamn afterlife."

"Stop," I said.

"Too dark?"

"Yeah, kind of. And my head hurts."

"You're probably hungry. I'll get you a snack." She dropped the file back down on the counter and came back with a package of chips. We both ate them until the doctor came back and I was casted up.

"I have to go, love," she said. "I have that big date."

I waved with my other hand, not in a cast. Sally raised a brow and grabbed a Sharpie from the counter. "Let me leave you with a last laugh," she said. She wrote something on the back of my cast, something I could barely see without twisting my body all around.

"There you are," she said. "I'll see you around."

"Have a good night."

The next day, she was gone.

I had theories about what happened to Sally. Most of the happier ones ended up with her living it up with the scar in a brand new car, him paying for her surgeries, and purchasing a mansion in Tahiti.

But I knew it was far more likely that the guy had shattered her skull instead.

When my cast came off six weeks later, I read about a body found in a local park. The doctor called me in from the waiting room before I could finish the article, so I tucked it under my hoodie and took it with me.

"Do you want to keep it?" the technician asked me, holding up my cast. "Sometimes people want to keep it."

I was about to say no, when I saw Sally's writing. She'd signed the cast before leaving.

I held open my backpack and the technician gave me the remnants of my cast. On the bus home, I read the newspaper about the dead body in the park. No head. No hands. No clothing.

"It's her," I told my roommate. I put the newspaper down on our table, but he barely looked up from his video game. "It's Sally. The body they found in the park."

"How do you know for sure?"

Because bones were all we had. I didn't say it aloud. I continued reading the article. The entire body hadn't been found, and at the rapid rate of decomposition, it wasn't likely they'd find any other pieces due to scavengers. Her pelvis, the one that she'd shattered and that doctors had to piece back together with metal and screws, must not have been found because there was no mention of tracing the serial numbers.

"DNA testing," a reporter said, "noted that the skeleton belong to a man."

My heart sunk. This was Sally, I was sure of it now. I still had a toothbrush from when she'd stayed over and we talked all night. But if I came forward with her DNA, her body would be released back into her family. They would give her back her old name, bury her in a family plot, and call her their Darling Son.

So I stayed quiet. I wrapped my cast with her last words on it with the newspaper that announced her death and hid it under my bed.

Six weeks after that, I walked by the local commentary and saw them burying a bunch of bodies in pine boxes. Unnamed, unclaimed by family, and given a pauper's funeral

My wrist ached for her again.

"You know, you have more masculinity in your pinky finger than most guys I know," Sally told me in group. This had been after I reiterated the story of my broken home in front of everyone without shedding a tear. Absent father, daddy issues. The standard stuff that therapists wanted to hear about transgender men.

And I *nailed* it.

"Thank you," I said.

"You know, that's not a compliment. Masculinity will be the death of this planet. So fragile. It snaps off like it's nothing and then we're left picking up the pieces."

I paused. My binder cut deep into my chest and I could barely move an inch without pain ricocheting through my body. My D-breasts were sandwiched across me, never moving. And that pain remained me of why I was here. "Masculinity is what I want, though. It's what I need to pass."

"What you want is a body," Sally said. "New skin. More hair in places you didn't have it before. A voice. A little less fat off your chest. You don't want masculinity. Most cis men don't want masculinity. It's something thrust upon you."

I didn't know what to say. I couldn't really talk with my binder so tight, anyway. I hoped my silence counted as a response. In most conversations with men, I had learned that it did.

"You want to get breakfast?" she asked. "I'm feeling like eggs. I think eggs would be good right now."

It was four in the afternoon, but I said yes. We talked all night and into the morning. I laughed harder than I had in weeks. The next day, when I woke up and saw bruises across my chest, I went to the emergency room.

"What have you been doing, Rachel?"

"It's... Ryan. My name is Ryan."

"What have you been doing?" The doctor asked without looking up from the x-rays. "You have four fractured ribs. Has someone been hurting you?"

"No," I said. "I've just been having fun."

"When the hyoid bone, located in the throat," the medical examiner from TV said, "breaks, it means the cause of death is usually strangulation."

I shut off the TV. Another crime drama had paraded out transgender women as set design when talking about a prostitute's death. Every single episode was the same, all the medical and legal information a rehashed version of the previous episode. When I was twelve, I used to find these shows comforting. Someone was killed. Medical science and detective work found the killer. And they were put away.

Now, at twenty-seven, everything seemed to ring hollow. Sally had been dead for months. There was no way anyone would ever find the scar with the car. Even if I came forward, I could barely make a dent in Sally's case file given what I knew. So I went to bed instead of watching TV.

I slept with a hand around my throat. Sick fever dreams that pinned me to the bed. Pressure on my chest, like someone was weighing my breasts down with sandbags. When the bone in my throat—hyoid, hyoid I repeated, named after the Greek word for U—snapped, my body shot awake.

And Sally stood in front of me.

Her bare feet didn't touch the floor. She was made up of light and gossamer, so thin I could see through her body and to the next wall. She wasn't wearing loud colours or sequins or pink eyeliner. Her hair was short, too brown, and cropped close to her head. She wore a jean collared shirt over jeans. One of the worst cardinal sins of fashion.

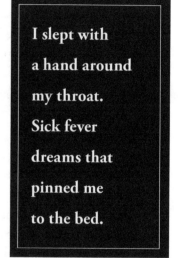

"Sally?"

"Ryan. You've gotta help me." Her voice was soft, but dry. She sounded far away; like she was trapped under glass or underwater. "I'm dead."

"I know. I'm sorry."

"Shut up. Sympathy is for the weak. I need you to do something."

"What?"

"You have to make me the Skeleton Key."

"What?"

"Skeleton Key," she repeated, voice softer. Her silhouetted outline disappeared against my bedroom wall.

She was gone. Again.

I touched my throat and looked at it in the mirror, expecting to find bruises. There was nothing. I stared up at the ceiling, repeating the words in my mind over and over again. Her blue demined madness splashed in front of me.

We have genders in the afterlife, I realized. *What a cruel, stupid fate.*

I made the jerk off motion with my hand. My wrist smarted from where I'd broken it. My ribs hurt from my binder earlier that day. And my hyoid bone still ached as if it had been snapped in two.

Had Sally been choked? I didn't know. I shouldn't care how she ended, only how she lived. That had been the motto at group when she disappeared. No one had had a funeral, excerpt for private eulogies we all had in our minds. To everyone else, Sally wasn't dead. Just gone.

A ghost.

I saw her—except not her--in front of me again. How do you get rid of ghosts? I Googled all the options on my phone and only came up with burning the bones, burying the body. None of which seemed to work for her. It wasn't that Sally was a ghost; it was that she wasn't the right ghost.

Make me the Skeleton Key. That was what she wanted. So I searched up that next. A skeleton key was a master key that could open any door, usually part of a hotel. It was also a novel by Stephen King, who Sally read voraciously.

"I'm always in waiting rooms for treatments," she'd say. "So you need a couple hundred thousand words of nonsense from King to keep you going."

Her voice was so clear in my mind I started to laugh again. Then I nearly cried when I remembered her rant about Carrie, the girl with telekinetic powers who went to prom. It was evidence that Stephen King was a little bit trans.

"What other apparent middle aged man writes a revenge fantasy using period blood and prom as the main M.O.? Come, *on*," Sally said. "That's total Venus envy."

Everything we touched, everything we read, became a little bit trans because we wanted it to be. Before Sally was a ghost, she was always haunting things.

So of course our bones were haunted. Of course they were already cursed. If a skeleton key opened all doors, could it also put her soul back together? If I found all of her bones, could I put Sally back together?

The thought kept me up until morning. Then I went for a drive.

I found a metal detector, the kind that beach combers use, from a pawn shop. I brought it to the local park where her body had been found. There were indentations in the grass from the spokes the crime scene unit must have used to put up barriers from the public. When nothing but bottle caps came up in this area, I expanded my search.

And found tire tracks. *From the scar with the car?* I wasn't sure and certainly didn't know enough about cars to be able to trace the treads. I followed them from a picnic area into the back woods. Months had passed, I told myself. I was unlikely to find anything more but bottle caps again. But the beach comber went off.

A screw. Metal, industrial strength. From her pelvis. I followed the beeping and came up with another pile of bones. Her pelvis was shaped like the hyoid bone, only bigger. U-shaped and caked with dirt and metal that kept it intact. Next to the pelvis, I saw scattered bones from a hand. I picked up her pinky and slipped it into my pocket. Warmth flooded me.

"Hi, Sally," I said. "I'm sorry."

I put what remained of her hands and other small bones that looked no more than stones into my backpack. Her pelvis slipped from my hands, shattering like it must have done years before. The bone shards fell down into a pattern, then rearranged themselves. They spelled out an address.

135 Stevenson Drive.

I looked it up on Google Maps. It was a hotel at the edge of town.

My car was the only one in the lot. A black man sat at the front desk, a thick red-covered book in front of him. He raised his eyes from the words as soon as I stepped inside. "Hello."

"Hi," I said. "I don't know if I'm in the right place."

"What do you need?"

"A skeleton key."

"Well, I need a skeleton."

"A whole one?"

"A piece of one will do. But your favourite piece."

"I'm... I'm very confused." The pinky finger in my pocket warmed again. The shards of her pelvis now were too dangerous to handle; I'd barely been able to put them in my backpack without cutting my thumbs to ruins.

The man behind the counter, teeth wide like china bowls, smiled. "You need to open a door and deliver a wandering soul, I'm guessing?"

I nodded.

"Good. Find that person's body. Bring me a little bit o' bone and I will give you the key to get to the other side. Deliver the rest of the bones to the portal--the door to the next world. Then your person will make it through."

"And she'll be better there?"

"What is she like right now?"

"Angry," I said. I touched my neck and he didn't seem fazed by it, like it happened all the time. "She's also not who she died as."

"Hmmm." He pondered this a moment. When he set the book he'd been reading down in front of him, I realized it was all blank pages. Nothing there but tiny pin pricks like Braille, expect that the man could see. He looked passed me, through me, down to my very bones themselves.

"How did the ghost appear to you?" he asked.

"As a man. But she's a woman."

"Her bones—"

"Her bones lied. She is a woman. I know her as one. She knows me as a man."

"Are you the only person who knows she's dead?"

"I think. Now. But someone found her body and they labeled her wrong."

"There you go. Our ghosts are only memories reread too many times until they manifest. So you need to counter the rumours with your facts. You need to bring her back to life."

"Can't I do that by pushing her through the portal? Bringing all of her bones here?" I asked, exhaustion seeping into my tone. I ached and wanted to sleep. I hadn't gone to my job in two days, and I had no sick days to draw from. "I just want her to rest."

"You need to counter with a memory. One that will last. That's why there are headstones. People read the name. Name stays alive. Right now she's anonymous. So you need to bring her back."

"Do I do this before or after I send her bones through the portal?"

"Either will do. But within twenty-four hours."

I glanced at the clock in his office. It said three PM, but it seemed so much later than that. "Okay. I can do that."

"Good. Now give me a bone."

I took the pinky out of my pocket and handed it over to him. He sniffed it and smashed it into dust. It fell into the book and dissolved into the pages. His eyes turned to black orbs.

"Thank you. You can go."

"But the key—you haven't given me anything."

"You need her skeleton. She is the key." He drew his pen and wrote down several words. "Here is the address. Bring her bones there and give her a headstone. Then she will be free."

> You don't deserve to think of awful people. They'll shrink and shrink and shrink out of your life if you don't think about them.

When I was nine, my father threw me down the stairs. I broke my first two toes and fractured my shin. As I waited with my mother in the ER, I started to see spots. We learned that he'd also cracked my skull, like he'd cracked my mother's years before.

The doctor who saw me was kind and spoke in an even voice. He told me random facts about this hospital, about the X-Men when he noticed my T-shirt, and then random facts about bones. Anything he could think of to keep me awake, so I didn't fall asleep and never wake up.

"You know," he said. "When you're born, you have almost three hundred bones. As you grow up, you get fewer, right down to two hundred and six. "

As I waited out my concussion, I also waited for my body to get bigger so I could break less. Instead, Social Services were finally called and my father was locked up.

I became the man of the house, then.

"Your father was awful," Sally said when I told her my version of the story. "You don't deserve to think of awful people. They'll shrink and shrink and shrink out of your life if you don't think about them. The good times will grow and grow and grow."

My shins ached again, like they had when I was nine, as I dug up Sally's body. Her grave was in the corner of the cemetery with little lightning and virtually no presence. It was dark enough, and warm enough at night now, so I could do this and not be caught.

At around midnight, I cracked open her casket and took out all the bones. I still had her hands from the park and her pelvis in a thousand pieces. The pinky had been used to pay her way. I had everything I needed... except for her head.

I ached as if it'd been split open. Could I get away without having her skull? Surely I had enough.

As I stacked her bones up in my backpack, I worried that she'd be forced to live her life as a headless horseman, haunting the playground and warning little children about the dangers of gender.

The address the man at the hotel had given me was an hour away in the middle of a lake. When no boat rental place was open, I hacked the locks, grabbed a boat, and sped out into the middle of the lake.

I dropped each one down and counted them up. The din of the mosquitoes sounded inside my head, but none of them bit me, as if I was protected by something. By the time I'd reached the end of the backpack, I tilted it open and scattered her bone dust on the surface. It dissolved. The water was blacker than the night around me. Nothing happened for a long time as I waited for the crushing feeling of my chest to disappear.

The lake started to bubble. White mixed with the black surface. And Sally's bones rose to the top. Her femur, her ribcage, and sections of her hands. They all floated.

"Oh no," I cried out.

Sally's jokes about her osteoporosis and how she was like a flightless bird thanks to her hollow bones rolled around in my mind. "Call me ostrich. Call me emu. If I keep eroding, maybe one day I'll fly away."

I started to sob.

"Sink, sink. Please go away. Please sink down."

I paddled back to the shoreline and found rocks, flat black ones used to skip across the surface. I dug through the sand, ravenous and desperate for something heavy to weight her body down and get her to the portal. The more I dug, the more I felt something take over my body. Dirt clung to my nails. My skin split on the rocks. I uncovered a stone so white, so pristine I thought it wasn't real.

I pulled out a skull from the sand on the shore. A skull with a small bullet hole in its centre, like the plug of a basin that let life slip through. I held Sally's skull in my hand and sighed.

"I have all of you now."

I filled her skull with rocks to weigh it down and got back into the boat. In the centre of the lake, I dropped her into the water. The skull cracked. More bones, tiny and numerous like a baby's, flew everywhere.

But she started to go down. Down and down and down into the water, Sally disappeared.

The lake was black again and still. The humming of mosquitoes turned to the humming of music. I still had one last piece to solve.

"You know," Sally said. "I don't think I want surgery anymore."

We lay back on the car from the scar she was dating. Cherry red, hood long and flat. The two had had sex on it, but she still thought it was better for lounging than fucking.

"So why go to group?" I asked. "Therapy is only there so you can talk out your demons before the knife cuts you open and repurposes the flesh."

"Oh, creative. Since when did you become the Adam from clay?"

"Since the doctors promised to make me but forgot to breathe life into me."

"You see, that's why I don't want surgery. I already have a life. I'm full of it." Sally grinned and nudged my shoulder. "And I really think I have found someone who likes my body the way it is."

"A fuck on the hood of the car is hardly a vow."

"Yeah, but I don't want to be a wife."

"What do you want to be?" I asked. "I mean who. Who do you want to be?"

"Sally. That's it. I don't ask for much."

All I thought of was how hard it was for me to be Ryan. Sally could forgo surgery, but she had an option. I could only have a penis crafted out of the skin of my thigh, called a franken-dick by most other trans men in group. I could only ever dream of having something I could reject. I always had to take whatever was handed to me.

"But you know," Sally went on, "I also go to group for you. Where else would I get such cutting commentary about the state of men?"

"The scar doesn't talk?"

"Oh, God no. Why would he? Masculinity makes them silent. Please learn from those mistakes."

I told her I would try. I knew those mistakes were the ones that had knocked me down stairs and broke my toes. Crushed my ribs and left me with purple bruises everywhere. Two weeks after the conversation on the scar's car, I'd be in the hospital with a broken arm.

I'd always break myself to make myself feel whole.

And Sally would be dead.

Both of us never fucking learned.

When Sally's body was under the water, I rowed to the shore. I picked up the piece of paper the man at the hotel had given me and a pen from the bottom of my backpack. I wrote down Sally's name. Her date of birth (give or take) and added that her favourite colour was pink. Hot pink.

I floated the paper into the water. Watched it dissolve. I checked the black water.

Nothing moved.

When it wasn't enough, I picked up my phone and called Sally's answering machine. There was still enough space. I listed off all the bones that I had broken and what I had learned from each one. Shin, toes, skull, ribcage, wrist, hyoid (if only in a dream). I was still talking when an orb of white light appeared in the middle of the pond. The light constituted itself, piece by piece, until Sally was formed.

She wore the same sequined top in bright pink she had on when she disappeared. Her hair was the same shade of bottled-blonde and down to her shoulders. She had no shoes, but her toes were painted in pink.

She waved at me. I waved at her. The wave turned into the jerking off motion, and I finally hung up the phone.

"Thank you," she said. "What a fucking relief."

"I hate that the after world has genders. This is the worse lottery I've ever seen."

She laughed, loud and throaty. It made the water ripple towards me.

"It sucks, but you do what you can. Remember what I said, right?"

I nodded.

"Good. 'Cause I gotta go," she said. "Never fall in love with men and their cars. And always speak up. Something else, too. Make my last words good, bro."

I waited until she disappeared under the water again. When I couldn't breathe, I thought I'd been choked again. Tears stung my face instead. I reached into my bag and pulled out the cast from my arm.

I left it in the hollow from where I'd dug up her skull. Her signature faced the dawn as it crept up over the trees along the lake. Water lapped at its surface, dissolving into nothing but dust. ◈

IMANI

WENDY HOWE

The priests said the holy breathe and live on through inscription.
From studies on the ancient dead.

Egyptian-braided, eyes ringed with kohl and linen gathered
with a grass belt, she feels the power of being brown skinned
and Nile long -- connecting an end with a beginning,
an upper class with a lower.

Today, she is boundless, unafraid to surpass
stop or yield, unafraid of being suddenly caught
or shot. She has already been there -- in the east section
of the city where blue gods lurk among its ruins
looking for those who look guilty. Where the closest thing
to a fountain is a hydrant busted while green clusters
in-between slabs of cracked pavement. Not to mention how pigeons
wade in damp shadows and debris. And to think

there once were papyrus leaves and an ibis scanning the river
to bless and clean its waters. Her ancient sisters knew
of his sacred instinct and worshipped the bird; their names are painted
with hers on a warehouse wall that overlooks the beach. And along with them,
those who persuaded her. Hand maidens of poverty who came
with white powder and a copper spoon. The flick of a lighter that slowly melted
gray matter into pure spirit. The burn-down of sun that eventually left
the girl as a depiction on cement.

WHAT IS CAST

WENDY HOWE

On the wall
of a half-burnt house
leaf shadows
palpitate.

Think of humming birds
(wound in flight)
pulling on moss and milkweed
to craft a nest,

or braided hair
shimmering in the sun
as a woman gathers
her bay berries and vine.

Wild things
she most boil and weave.
to survive.

On the wall
of the half-burnt house,
frost spackles
some of the cracked stucco.

And it's known
the small birds
have already flown south

and the woman has passed
through the black pines
preparing to shape
her source of light and storage.

Enough candles for prayer,
enough baskets to keep
her salvaged bones.

CARABOSSE

WENDY HOWE

(For Marian in the ICU)

A dark bird lands in the leafless tree
with a berry in its beak,
a bitter snack. In the old tale
a fairy's bane. The fruit
neither red nor black
but maroon --like something that bled
in her brain causing
the closed eyelids, the voiceless tongue,
the theft of awareness
that leaves a woman sleeping
and hooked to spindles with paper rings.

Around her, the municipal clocks
have not stopped ticking. Daylight
still unravels with the chill
of late winter; and the city spins
its thread into a pattern
of people working, walking dogs
or watching crows suture the sky,
the long river glittering beneath
half frozen and half- alive.

STANDING IN THE EDGELAND

WENDY HOWE

The wind wants to tear down my fence
loosening the palings and pushing forth
the openness of an edgeland, my garden spilling
into a field of Joshua trees. Coyotes, jack rabbits
and others could enter -- but the dust needs no fallen barrier;
it never did. It carries secrets of the land
and of those buried beneath, the pungent smell
of drought. I'm reluctant to breach this grove of trees
sheltering ghosts and ravens, the tribe of my sins
and those messengers who would tell me what has been cast. Science
calls this place a high desert habitat -- with little rain
and four seasons. I know better. It's where you come to listen
on the border of nowhere and everywhere, wanting to solve
the riddle of what sings in your bones, the disquiet that quarantines,
renders you vulnerable -- to imagination and what she hides
in her hood of fur. Her most primal state.

BIRD OF DIASPORA

WENDY HOWE

The wicked have burned our books
and with the charred words, they have turned
our soul to ash. If there is mercy
among the elements, let a spirit
paste and mold those cinders
into a mourning dove. Then leave the bird
to nest in a fig tree. When the weather warms,
and the humid wind causes its feathers
to molt, there will be whisperings
of who we were:

the woman who stitched
linen and leather in her house
to make a living,

who braided her hair and bread
into something strong and beautiful,
a lattice work
of heritage and wheat,

the man who studied
the precision of scales
and the text of ancient scrolls,

who lit an oil lamp
and played his songs of experience
on a violin,
the child who spun
his or her mind
into a universe of letters and stars,

who learned how to permeate
and assume the shape

of unknown things like water

and people who thought
they could blend
into a city of new ideas

while the silt of Israel
was still settling
in the riverbed of their veins.

flash fiction

A Cup of Chai
and Never After

SAMIA AHMED

ou are twenty one, a senior. *Your lips my lips apocalypse*, Cigarettes After Sex plays in the background; a soothing voice often helps you concentrate, while your girlfriend lays next to you, with her pink tutu, her purple spandex, her too-thick-eyeliner that smudges a little from the ends. This one is blonde, reminds you of butterscotch and honey every time you kiss her. She has a nice body. You have hope for this one. It lasts a month and a half. She sleeps with your best friend, and your roommate, and your roommate's best friend.

*****

This one is a brunette, she paints her lips in shades of orange and sometimes burgundy, depending on the color of her bra. You figured that out the second night, after you ice-skated. You tell her she is pretty before you sleep, every night, because she is, and she should know. This one you marry, not in the church though, since you both aren't religious. She is agnostic you are spiritual, or somewhere in that zone. You tell her she is pretty, but she goes back to sleep without saying anything. She says she is bored then moves out. You get a text during class, you are late paying alimony. You sleep with someone prettier, there's more brown in her hair than the last one.

Download this dating app, this has the best ones, your best friend tells you.

You do it, go out, and meet a nice Indian one.

*****

This one you cannot place, her hair changes colors depending on the time of the day. At midnight, it reflects the silver of the moon sliding through the edges of your doorway that opens up to the balcony. At noon it's honey, at four it's auburn. At six, she is at home, in your kitchen cooking a curry. You stereotype her, she breaks every one of them. She asks a lot of questions, you answer them. You learn how to say *Namaste*. She laughs and walks away.

You go to India where she shows you the tree behind which she kissed for the first time. She shows you her school and you meet all her friends. You stand in a corner awkwardly as they talk in *Hindi*, you wonder what a delightful girl she is, and you think you are lucky.

You come back, she is still there. You think this one will last, this one will last a lifetime. You adopt a puppy, name her *Megha*. She says it reminds her of the rain. She reminds you of rain. But the rain is cold and wet. You wonder. You fall out of love. She takes *Megha* with her. You forget how to say *Namaste*.

short story

A GALLERY OF MY OWN

SHANNA MERCERON

nother farm fired me, the third one in ten years. They all hired me for the experience I had working summers on my aunt and uncle's farm in my adolescence. After high school, I worked on a chicken farm first, upgraded to pigs, and then back to chickens. I did my job right, I did it fast, I had finesse, and the blood didn't bother me. I think that's why they fired me. My last boss told me I should be more clinical, said he didn't like the dreamy look in my eyes with my hands wrapped around a chicken's neck.

I stood on Dana's front lawn. We were going for a walk tonight. Her idea; she was attempting to make contact with me. I wondered if it bothered her, my distance. I thought about my uncle. I missed him, I missed his farm, and I missed his hands. He had my favorite pair of hands. My uncle handcrafted southwestern jewelry and had a booth at the weekend flea market where he sat and made necklaces and earrings in front of people. He said his jewelry was more likely to sell if they thought he was Cherokee or Apache, so he tied his hair in a long braid and sat out in the sun to encourage a tan. He wore a lot of fringe. I should have been ashamed of him, but he did so well for himself, gathering crowds while silver and turquoise bent to the will of his fingers. I was captivated by the way he moved his hands. They were large and rough, yet they handled the tiny and delicate jewelry with care. His skin was calloused, sometimes marred by small pinpricks of blood where he poked himself with wire or his tools. My uncle could have a complete conversation with someone while he worked with his hands. They knew what they were doing; they did their own thinking. His eyes were dreamy too, but I thought his hands were his best feature.

Dana locked her front door and waved as she made her way toward me. Her hair swung as she walked, brushing the belt loops in her tight jeans. She grinned at me, her green eyes as bright as her smile, and I tried to mimic her expression. I unclenched the scarf I was wringing in my hands like a chicken's neck and tossed it back on.

"It's so cold!" She said, gripping my hands. "My knuckles are starting to crack." I traced the crosshatched red marks in her dry skin. I wished the blood hadn't dried. It had been a while since I'd touched human blood.

"I have lotion in my bag," I said, reaching for my tote, wanting to rub it into her palms, break the cracks, but Dana shook her head.

"Let's walk, best to get our blood flowing," she said. I could only agree. She looped her arm through mine and we started the walk downtown, the cobblestone streets bathed in the light of golden hour. She led the conversation, telling me about the phone call she had with her mother and the plumber who stopped by on Tuesday. I supplied head nods and the occasional two-word commentary.

"What's bothering you?" Dana asked, as we turned onto the row of art galleries. It wasn't my silence that tipped her off; that was nothing new. She just had a sense when something was wrong. I wished I had that intuition.

"I got fired," I said. No point in holding back.

"Again?" Dana wasn't surprised. She'd known me since middle school, she'd known my spacy and disconnected ways. She knew I wasn't the best with people. She pursed her lips, holding a thought in her mouth. "I think I could get you a job," she eventually said. We slowed our walking. "They told me the team has money for an assistant. You'd get to work with me. I'd teach you."

Dana was a personal trainer for the city's minor league hockey team. She invited me to watch the games with her, but I couldn't imagine myself in an environment with so many emotional people. I thought it would just make me feel more isolated; I wouldn't be able to connect.

"That would be very gracious of you," I said. I could work with the players, though. Bandage some knuckles, soak up a bloody nose. I felt a smile work on my face. This could be a good change from the farms.

"When could I start?" I said. We wandered into the first gallery, a collection of blown glass in primary colors.

"I'll mention it to my supervisor tomorrow, and I'll let you know." Dana looked at each piece as if she was going to buy it, but I knew she wouldn't. She launched into detail about all the players and which one I might be interested in and which one she had a date with on Friday. I checked out, unable to follow the names, getting lost in the rush of her words. I tuned her out and explored the gallery.

"Laura?" Dana was hovering over my shoulder, watching as I ran my fingers over the rim of a bowl. I didn't remember walking over to it.

"I think I need to go home." I moved away from the bowl, my limbs heavy. Loneliness was building in me, and Dana's company couldn't solve it. I wanted to tell her things I'd never told anyone, but she was in a good mood. She didn't have a void yawning inside her. She wasn't tempted by impulses.

Dana opened her mouth to convince me to stay with her, but my expression changed her mind. She wrapped me in a hug and rubbed her hands on my back. "See you soon, yeah?" she said.

"Soon," I said. I walked out of the gallery, and kept walking until I was far away enough from her to let out a scream.

As I moved back home, I had to pass the boutiques and art galleries again. The city had two art districts, and I purposely situated my home close to this one. On weekends, the sidewalks were crowded with artists selling their wares, reminding me of the weekends spent with my uncle.

Night had fallen, and the street was deliciously empty. Free of judging eyes and crowded sidewalks, I prowled through it like it was my own. I passed my favorite gallery, the one with animal heads nailed to the wall that Dana found distasteful, and I continued down the street, sometimes stopping to peer in at the art, or merely peering at my own reflection. My blonde hair was tucked into my coat, my eyes dark in the glass, but I could see that there was pinkness in my cheeks. I tried on Dana's smile from earlier, but grimaced when I saw it on my own face.

There was a gallery still open, despite it being past business hours, and I didn't remember ever seeing the gallery before. It was as if my mind had created it, in an attempt to quench some unspoken desire to not go home yet. I stepped inside, looking at the canvas closest to the door. It looked like a crime scene photograph, with staged bodies wearing masks and holding strange props. Random body parts were worked into the artistic background. I peered at the canvas next to it and took in a similar scene: two women in masks, their skin deathly pale, sitting in chairs, their arms held up by fishing line, reaching for each other. Teddy bears sat on their laps. Their legs looked like they were stitched on. I checked to see if a gallery assistant was in the room, but I was alone with the daring and macabre pictures. I stepped out and continued with my walk home, my heart trying to turn me back around, telling me to spend the night there.

I stopped again when I heard music playing, slicing through the icy night. I turned on the street behind the galleries, where a few garage door storage rooms were rolled open. Passing by a man and woman sorting through large picture frames and arguing passionately, I wandered through the back alley before I located the space with the music. The beats were loud and cutting, causing my heart rate to kick up in an effort to keep rhythm with the erotic melody. The garage door was all the way up, the room converted into a workspace.

Inside the studio, harsh lights shone from the ceiling and mannequins were stacked in a corner. Plastic tarp covered most of the walls and floor, red paint splattered or pooling on them. A man wearing a paint-covered apron and science-goggles bobbed his head along to the music as he assembled an art piece on a large steel table in front of him. I couldn't make out what he was working on. He had a few blue buckets stacked on the table. The man was tall, with wild, curly blonde hair sticking out in a halo around the goggles' strap. He wore latex gloves too, and his shoes were wrapped up in protection from the paint. It looked like he took his work seriously.

"Hey there!" he said, shouting over the music. He gave me a wave and went back to his work. I hesitated on the threshold of his space.

"You're an artist?" I asked. I didn't want to leave yet. I wanted to stay with the music and the paint for a moment. I felt a little less lonely here; there was something familiar about the space. The wind picked up, blowing a harsh gust down the alley. I instinctively took a step inside the studio to avoid the cold. It was surprisingly warm inside. Maybe it was the lights.

The man snapped his head up from his work again to evaluate me. "You know you're tres-passing, right?" he said, a frown forming on his face. He set down the tool he had in his hand. I realized it was a knife. I stood my ground.

"It's getting cold out," I blurted. The man snapped the gloves off his hands. He set them on the table and came around, crossing the room to meet me.

"Can I help you with anything? My gallery is the next street over. This stuff isn't for sale yet."

He looked to be maybe thirty, thirty-five. The stubble on his jaw gave his face a golden glow. I couldn't look at his eyes; the reflection in the goggles was off. I casted my eyes down to his hands, now bare. They were lovely. Tan and scarred, with paint layered under the fingernails. His veins arced seductively at the knuckles, just like my uncle's had. I wonder if this man only ever used them to create. I flashed my eyes back up to his.

"Just looking," I said. The man held my gaze for an intense moment. His eyes flicked down to his hands and he tucked them behind his back.

"Would you like to see what I'm working on?" He started walking back toward his table. The music was still so loud. I nodded my head and followed, stepping deeper into the studio, inhaling the sharp scent of the sawdust and paint I was now standing on. It smelled like someone had just turned on a sprinkler in the morning, sulfuric and unpleasant.

"Oh yeah, watch your boots, it's a little messy over here." He guided me over to his worktable and gestured in a ta-da fashion at the mess before us. He had a mannequin leg on the table, paint cans filled with crimson paint, brushes, and knives scattered over the tabletop. The buckets were filled with other legs and arms, and maybe some other parts I didn't want to see.

"Halloween sales are the best," he said.

The leg looked real. I stepped back, almost slipping in the paint. I knocked into a bucket on the floor, this one filled with plastic ears, their stumps red.

"Try to stand in the sawdust, it soaks it all up." The man laid his hands on the leg before him and glided over the skin, drumming his fingers absentmindedly. "I told you I wasn't finished," he said.

I fought to keep my expression neutral, and nodded my head. "I should go." I started for the alleyway. "Nice meeting you!" I said, tossing the words over my shoulder with my scarf as I tightened it around my neck.

"My name is Travis," he said.

I turned around and he smiled devilishly. He lifted his hands and slipped his gloves back on. He smacked the latex and winked at me. "Come back anytime."

I almost bumped into a trashcan as I hurried down the alley, the streetlights in it flickering off one by one.

I let the gusting wind carry me home.

That night my dreams were filled with paint covered fingers trailing marks up and down my skin. But when they gripped my ears and tugged, I snapped awake. I thrusted my hand under my pillow and gripped the cool steel of my knife, stroking it until my breathing quieted.

In the morning, I woke to bloodstained sheets. I hovered in the bathroom with my underwear around my ankles, my monthly visitor staining the blue cotton rust. I shoved a hand into myself, buried it up to my wrist, and then pulled the hand out. I held it up in front of the mirror, the pale flesh turned red, and a clump of uterine lining stuck to a finger pad. Painted red and glowing under the florescent light, I could see the scars on the back of my hand from the nails of chickens that scratched, shining through clean and white. I could see how small my hand looked; how, really, it looked like it couldn't do anything at all. I brought my fingertips to my nose and inhaled. It smelled of iron and summers with my aunt in the barn.

> I think she knew that I liked the power of holding necks between my hands and feeling their pulse flow and stop under my fingers.

My aunt had divine hands, too. But where my uncle had hands that created beauty, my aunt had hands that brought death. They were brutal, with sharp knuckles and nubby nail beds. She taught me how to kill, pluck, and cook chickens in the summers of my teenage years. I think she knew that I liked the power of holding necks between my hands and feeling their pulse flow and stop under my fingers. I think she saw something of herself in me. I envied her violence. I envied how she fit with my uncle, so soft and creative. They were ferocity and gentleness coming together. I craved that fitting.

One night, when I was watching a movie with my uncle on the couch, I kept glancing to his hands as they twisted a ring around his fingers. The silver was glinting in the light of the soy market candles burning on the mantle. He caught my distraction and put the ring on the coffee table. I reached over and put his hand on my upper thigh, my skin prickling with the thrill from the weight of it. I rubbed circles on the back of his hand, calming the muscles that had tensed. I guided his hand in deeper.

"No." My uncle stood up, stood over me, casting a shadow of shame on my face, on the heat that burned in my core. I hoped he would hit me. Curl his fingers into a fist, bust my lip. What a beautiful mess we could make. But he left the room. My aunt never invited me back to the farm after that.

In the evening, I found myself scrolling through radio stations, trying to find something similar to what Travis was playing. Dana had met me for lunch; I could start with the team on a trial basis. I spent my day prepping for my new job by researching the rules of hockey while his song played on repeat in the back of my mind. After my finger was sore from hitting the seek button so much, I gave up, and left my stereo to go for a walk. I sought Travis out, followed the familiar route to the storage room alley, but hesitated once I passed the galleries. I knew something about him wasn't right. Something about him seemed dangerous and powerful, but also searching. Like he was lonely in the dark too. It was that feeling that continued to power my footsteps to his studio.

I knew he saw me staring at him, watching from the alleyway, the sun setting behind me, accusations about to leak from my lips. I wanted to question him. My imagination came up with all sorts of explanations and fantasies for the blood in his studio and the body parts he kept in buckets. But when I arrived that night, looking for answers, he was brushing the hair of a head on his table.

It's just a mannequin, it's just a mannequin, it's just a mannequin.

Pushing my intrusive thoughts away, I became absorbed in the beauty of his hands as they executed each stroke of the brush through the hair. He handled each tangle delicately, only tensing slightly at the wrists. After he set the brush on the table, he braided the hair, the auburn locks twisting in his delicate fingers. When he finished the braid, he rubbed the tip of his finger against the bristled end.

I let my eyes wander up to his face, his eyes meeting my own. He picked up the head and moved it to the end of the table, the braid dangling over the edge.

The next night I arrived without any expectations. If I wanted answers, I would simply continue to observe. And he let me.

I watched him maneuver in his meat shop. I watched when he chose to use gloves and when he chose to forgo them, when a human specimen was spread out on his table, and when he used his bare hands to better stretch the skin before cleaving it with a blade. It was still fresh. Blood sprayed up and hit the walls, flowed to the floor, and flecked his face. Nothing like the chickens. A drop hung from his bottom lip. He licked it away.

I stopped standing in the alley when I watched him. No one ever passed through, but if someone did it would look strange to see me standing in its center, enchanted by a wicked force in a garage. So I stood with a hip pressed against his table, sensible shoes on my feet, and a desire to wear sunglasses at night to mask the thirst I was sure my pupils held. But I resisted. I felt like I didn't have to hide.

I determined that his mannequins and props were for show. I didn't know where he got his bodies. Travis began to smoke a cigar in my company, growing more comfortable with the eyes that traced his figure and counted each drop that hit the floor. I wondered what he thought of me, if my silence weighed on him, but I was still working out what to think of him.

On the third day of my presence in his studio, two men rolled up with a cart. A tarp covered it, but I could smell what the cart contained, even with the cigar smoke snaking up my nostrils.

They knocked against the garage door, catching Travis's attention. Travis waved an arm and the men pushed the cart into the studio. One of the men flicked his eyes over to me and raised an eyebrow to Travis. He shrugged. The men removed the tarp and placed a dead woman's body on one of the steel tables. Travis handed them a bloodstained envelope and the men pushed the cart out of the studio and down the alley. I looked over to Travis as he ran a single finger along the curve of the woman's calf. If Travis didn't think I was a threat, I decided he wasn't one either.

But the following evening when I arrived at the studio, the garage door was rolled down with a padlock chained to it. I thought about pounding on it, screaming Travis' name in tempo to the beats of the music that I couldn't get out my head. I would not let this be taken away from me so soon. I contemplated kicking at the lock until it snapped. I shoved a fingernail into its crevice, attempting to pick it open. My nail broke off and I hissed with pain, bringing the break to my mouth, sucking the blood that bloomed on my nail bed. A breeze coasted through the alley, teasing the hair out of my braid, pulling at a strand tucked behind my ear. With it, the wind brought Travis' song. I followed the music, moving like a ghost called to the void, a magnet tugging me in a dark direction.

The music was playing from his gallery a street over. The gallery that seemed to appear overnight, that always had its door open, the gallery with the lurid photographs of dead people. I stepped inside, my internal magnet sending a buzz of pleasure through me when I saw Travis standing in front of one of the canvases, the goggles gone, instead a pen pinned behind an ear, and his hands tucked behind his back. His fingernails had dried blood layered underneath them.

"What is your name?" he said. He didn't turn to look at me. He lifted a hand and stroked a shadow on the flesh of the canvas.

"My name is Laura." I walked to stand next to him.

"What do you think, Laura?" He gestured at his photograph. In it, a woman with braided auburn hair was suspended upside down from the ceiling, her arms tied with rope against her chest. Chains stretched between her head and neck, connecting them. Her braid brushed the floor. She was naked, but she wore a masquerade mask, and piles of dresses littered the ground below her, chains wrapping the dresses together, and hands crawling out of spaces in the gowns.

"It's beautiful," I said. It was. I wanted it hanging in my foyer, greeting the few guests that visited me. I could invite my aunt and uncle, show them I've changed. See, I would say, this is what I've been drawn to all along.

Travis lifted a hand and gripped the end of my own braid. "I thought you would like it," he said. I wished I had nerve endings in my hair so I could feel his touch. I turned my body closer to him, wanting to join our bodies and push and pull them together with each beat of his maddening music.

"Where do your specimens come from?" I asked. I found myself choosing my words carefully. I didn't want to offend; I didn't want him to think I couldn't handle this. His hands were tucked behind his back again and I wished I could see them. I wanted to hear his answer as I gazed at the blood under his fingernails. I didn't care if he moved his hands to wrap them around my throat.

"Some people want to be beautiful even in death," he said.

"Do you ever kill them?" The words left my lips before my mind gave permission to the tongue. He placed a fist under his chin and tucked an arm under the elbow. Considered me. His hands were chapped. I could see the place where his stubble brushed the rough edges of his knuckles and I wondered if it itched. Would he let me scratch it? I gnawed on the inside of my lip until I drew blood, the taste occupying me in his silence.

"I'm an artist, Laura," he said at last.

I released my lip and the fist on my heart loosened. "What do people think of your art?" I asked, my hands twitching at my sides in anticipation of the answer.

"They wonder where I get such limber and amenable models." He gave me a wide grin, breaking through all the knots and tangles that kept me at arm's length. He reached for me, and brushed a hand along my jaw, sparking pleasure against my skin. "Would you like another look at my studio?"

I could only nod my head.

> I knew I was supposed to wear gloves, but there is beauty in washing blood off my hands.

I knew I was supposed to wear gloves, but there is beauty in washing blood off my hands. The way the warm water melts stains off my skin and swirls them down the drain, goopy and pink. It's hardest to get the blood out of my cuticles. This I had forgotten. Blood seems to cling in the seams, burying itself in the tiny crevices by my nails and sometimes, even after minutes of scrubbing, the blood will remain, a crimson ring in my nail beds. I started painting my fingernails red. If I couldn't scrub all the blood out, at least it looked like a bad paint job, not a crime scene. They didn't have to be beautiful.

Travis wore gloves. I liked to watch him snap his gloves on before he began his work. His gloves were powder blue and so tight; I could see the bulges of his veins through the latex. Sometimes later, after, when he wanted to touch me, he would leave them on and the blood-slick gloves would glide over my body but wouldn't leave a single print; messy red streaks of desire painting me new. But mostly I wish he didn't wear any gloves at all. I liked watching his fingernails pierce and tear flesh; I liked watching the roll of his fingers when he stretched the skin, when his hands would tighten their vise grip before blade cut through bone.

I liked my new job. I would arrive early to watch the practices, hovering in front of the glass, watching skates lacerate the ice, bodies crash into each other, and tasting the violence hanging thick in the air.

Dana taught me how to properly wrap knuckles, but it pained me to do it. To hold hands capable of such art and force, and cover them up, cover up their blood and scars. Their mess told stories, and I painted over them in white. Some of the players attempted to befriend me, but I watched the way they looked at Dana, and it wasn't the way they looked at me. I was nothing but a dim reflection of her, and I minded my business. This I had learned. My aunt told me to learn my place, and even once I did, to never come back. But Travis had welcomed me into his space. I was his assistant, but not a muse. I would not be a muse. A muse inspires others to create art. I was in the game to make art of my own. Maybe I would make Travis my muse. Maybe he wouldn't resist like my uncle had.

After high school, I had rented a space in a barn of the first farm that hired me, my first summer on my own. The farm was a mile from the flea market that operated in a field every weekend. The field was right alongside a major road, and visitors stopped to buy wares or stretch their legs. I went to the market every Saturday. I woke at dawn, killed my chickens, and then walked alongside the edge of the road until I reached the flea. I knew where his booth was. I had the route memorized; I worked through the maze until I reached him, past the leather belts and phone screen repair, next to the hand-woven rugs and frozen lemonade stand.

I kept my distance, but I was close enough to see him. To see his eyes, to see his hands. My aunt stood over his shoulder, like a predator guarding her prey. She reported me. Said a girl with bloody hands was prowling through the stalls.

Not long after that, the farm fired me and I found pigs to be better company. Pigs were a lot like humans. They knew when it was their death day, and I appreciated the challenge. I almost told Travis about my pigs but I didn't.

"I showed Dana your work. She called it gruesome," I said to Travis, handing him a bone saw. *She doesn't see it the way I do.*

"I'd say that's accurate." Travis brushed his fingers over mine and then gestured for me to step back.

"Don't you ever worry though? That you'll be questioned?" I watched his shoulders tense. I still wasn't sure how he pulled this all off. How this didn't weigh on him. Where the men with the cart came from and went.

"We're having this conversation again?" he asked me. He stepped away from his work and wrapped his arms around me.

"I know what I'm doing. You have nothing to worry about." He ran his hands down my arms, then up and over my hair. He brushed his knuckles against my cheek, smearing blood in their wake. He grazed his lips over my forehead, down my nose, and over to my ear. He bit my lobe, hard enough to draw blood, but I didn't make a sound. His lips touched my neck, he pressed his teeth to my carotid, and I fought back a moan. He hooked his arms under my legs and lifted me up, bringing me to the steel table. He placed me down on it gently, so gently, and I felt the blood that was still on it start to seep into the back of my shirt. I leaned further into it.

"The messier it is in here, the better," he grumbled, his face buried in my neck again. "We artists aren't clean."

Over the music, I could hear wheels rolling on asphalt. I turned my head and saw two men pushing a cart of frames down the alley. One lifted a hand and waved to Travis, winking at him.

"What have you learned about hiding in plain sight?" Travis asked me. He gave me his hands, letting me hold them and bring them to my mouth. They were two honed instruments of brutality and beauty. I wanted to swallow them whole, make them a part of me.

"Everything," I said, whispering against his skin.

I moved to the city to put distance between myself and my past. On the long drives out to the farms, I had often contemplated how I could have changed the night I put my uncle's hand on me. But the only thing I would change is his reaction.

My time spent with Travis seemed to exist in another world. We were in his studio, we were in the gallery, we were staging photographs in a warehouse, we were falling into my bed, or his, but usually mine; I never wanted him to tell me to leave.

But one day on the drive back from the warehouse, we stopped for groceries. He let me push the cart, and wandered at my side, sipping from a can of cola. He flicked off the pull-tab and gave it to me. I clenched it in my fist and steered the cart with my wrists. Travis wanted cherries, so we got cherries. He buried his fingers in the bag and ate a few. I didn't see him spit out any pits.

I lingered in the meats, looking at the yellow packaging for chicken and pink for pork. I thought about telling Travis about the different cuts of meat, but I didn't. I selected a few pounds of ground beef and moved on.

I decided I wanted pretzels to munch on for the drive home. We still had a ways to go back to the city. I turned my cart down an aisle and it collided with another cart around the bend.

"Oh! I am so—" my words trailed off. My uncle stood in front of me, gripping the handle of his shopping cart as hard as I was gripping mine. His knuckles were white. I wanted him to release the bar. I wanted his skin to turn back to pink and reveal how much they might have aged. He wore three turquoise rings on his right hand, and the wedding band on the left. I tensed, looking for my aunt but she wasn't with him.

"Laura," he said, my name coming out in a breathy gust.

"This is Travis," I said. "My partner." I lifted my chin to Travis. He quickly understood the situation, and swooped in, dropping his empty soda can into the cart. He shook hands with my uncle.

"Where is she?" I said.

My uncle's face tensed. "She stayed in the car."

I nodded. "Well, good to see you." I stuck out my own hand for him to shake. I didn't think he would hug me. He took my hand and then gasped, dropping my hand like it was on fire. The pull-tab that had imbedded itself into my palm as I gripped the cart, fell out of the indent of my hand and onto the tile.

A rush of blood bloomed on my uncle's palm.

"I didn't mean for that to happen. I had forgotten…"

My uncle took his cart and turned away. I watched him go.

When Travis and I moved through the parking lot, grocery bags in hand, I looped my arm through his, leant my head on his chest. I made a joke so he would smile. I laughed as prettily as I could.

I knew my aunt was in a car, somewhere, watching.

I watched Travis sleep that night, curled up in my bed, his hands tucked under the pillow like a child. He looked peaceful; I wondered if he slept sounder at my house, if somehow I managed to bring something to his life that he was craving.

I moved my face closer to his, so his hot sleepy breath caressed my cheeks. I checked the rhythm of his sleeping, determined that he had fallen deep. Reaching under the pillow, I carefully pulled his hands out, and laid them out on my chest for easy viewing. I inspected every inch of them, made sure the nicks and scars were still there, the lines etched into his palms were the same, and I inhaled their rich metallic scent that never seemed to go away. I thought about pulling out the knife that I kept under my own pillow, just in case, and cutting them off at the wrists right then and there. Limbs are much easier to manage once they're apart from their body. This I now knew. I could do anything with the hands then. They would truly be mine. I could suck each finger until they pruned and bury them inside me whenever I wished. I would keep them in a glass case, just for looking, because I knew I would touch them so much they would fall apart. But I knew how to preserve them, too. Stick them in a vat of formaldehyde. I could have his hands forever. The first in my collection. I would come for my uncle's next. I had already drawn his blood. I could have a gallery of my own.

I slid a hand under my pillow for the knife. I imagined his blood flowing over my hands like silky water. Once I cut them off, it would be hard for Travis to kill me without hands. But then again, the hands wouldn't be moved by him anymore. Would severing the cord erase their beauty?

Travis stirred and turned onto his side, taking his hands with him. Their weight was lifted off my chest, but I only felt heavier. ❦

TEAL SCREEN DOOR

DAN A. CARDOZA

It's platinum November, the smell of the Fourth of
July BBQ lingers, even the scent of missing you.

The chipped teal is emotive. Who knew grandpa
could speak the linguistics of acrylic some twenty
years gone.

Last summer the hinges swelled like a busy
molecule conventional, tightening the guiro and
crackle like a caw in a crow.

When you died I got drunk on a bench and smoked
unfiltered Camels into the tar of night. I imagined
the brass door knob changed channel's every time I
took a leak.

The wafts of dust in the screen smelled sweet like
the sky and placenta and stale whiskey I drank at
our failed wedding, the purification of funerals
never quiet done.

I awake in the dawns early light from all the white
noise.

CRYSTAL VASE

DAN A. CARDOZA

Art is magic delivered from the lie of being truth.
Theodor W. Adorno

The flowers I clutch are not so much an enigma,
at least to me. It is my hyaline avocation.

My affirmation, entrustment of emotion,
witnessed through my crystal lens of equal
proportion, the science of art, the art of science.

If your palette is a bloom of joy that I
articulate, in all its telling, then of course I say
long stem red roses should do. They bode
longevity of life, but can too soon be forgotten in
their allure of eye-candy & light.

Conversely, the hypnotic orchid, though short-
lived, is not so effortlessly abandoned. I'd say in
matters of beauty, of la vie & de mort, there is no
enigma as to apportionment. Hands down, it is
the orchid's peloria of dark stained lips that can
only be entrusted to hush, maybe subdue
eternity's exquisite moments of suffering.

COUNTING FISH

DAN A. CARDOZA

Leanne kept watch at the river, she seldom spoke, and
if she did it was to request just about anyone in her
way to kindly move from her view.

She seemed somehow to know how many fish and
fins and scales in the river flowed. It was not like
counting she just knew.

Someone proposed she had a fish net in her thoughts
that calibrated movement, maybe notion. Family
suggested it was an unproductive bad habit to kill
time.

Her younger brother, who she often spoke to when
they were alone, hesitated to offer suggestions; after
all, she refused to teach him to swim.

WINTER TIME LOVE

DAN A. CARDOZA

Loss moves mountains even buried in snow. It's a seasonal
show for the living, dressed in trendy black. Bring your dead
it's winter time, love. We are never alone.

I have support of a hospice worker or so-called Death Doula.
She can make you eat distraction like M&Ms, and guffaw at
her gallows humor. I am so impressed, Jesus, she cooks dying
like raw microwave casserole. I eat it with bad manners.

We are convinced he's talking to Elvis, who somehow learned
to croon on the ceiling. He loops a-hunk, a hunk of burning
love. Unimpressed, Herr Nurse says the funeral director will
help me bathe and groom the deceased now nameless, all
because

time grows death like weeds. When done, I close the laced
window, his melody gone because even the wind is done with
my father's song. 'It's winter time love," Just rusty crepe paper
lyrics, rustling its guiro leftover leaves in the dawn.

Someone light the damn fire we need a pyre to burn the
kindling of guilt and indifference, or just because it's perfectly
cold. Ashamed of my detection of living, I'll fit as tight as a
shadow into a midnight glove, and conjure tomorrow a Mardi
Gras, obliged to don a Fat Tuesday mask.

IDEA

DAN A. CARDOZA

He's guilty. Thatch the pyramid with more
pitchy oak. A crime was committed, to that
we all agree, and we are almost certain it's a
felony. Someone has to burn.

An anonymous voice in the crowd yells, "Are
we sure, beyond a reasonable doubt, that he
had an opinion?"

No answer was needed, the crowd pressed
forward, toward the mosh pit, the way they
used to in Aberdeen, at the Kurt Cobain
clubs. The air sparked lighters.

Then a woman yelled, begged let him speak,
let him speak? Some answers by thumbing
light. But it happened, the way few miracles
do, silence smothered the angry, like a
damp / dark cloud before rain.

In raspy Guiro vocals, he pleased, "What is
my crime? It was only an idea."

Just after he spoke, a new religion was born,
and like most, it was born in pyre, heaven the
ladder it climbed.

Long after the burning was done, long after
the wind whipped out his ashes, in the dawn's
early light, someone screamed, "Rock, Paper,
Scissors!"

Only the few found knees.

A Logical Explanation

MARISA CRANE

1 've been in denial about her metamorphosis for weeks, but this morning I can no longer ignore the fact that my girlfriend, Camila, is slowly turning into me. Now, what to do about it?

***

First, a Bumble date. She'd looked stunning. We'd talked all night, closed the bar down. I remember wishing with everything I had that she wouldn't turn out like all the rest.

Two weeks later, we'd become official and she'd begun sacrificing her own needs to meet mine.

One evening I'd come home from a business trip to find that she'd skipped work all week to re-design my apartment into my fantasy home, complete with a vintage 16mm camera and projector in my living room. The Hound of the Baskervilles (the 1939 version, which is the only version worth watching) was playing on the pull-down screen across from the projector.

"You really didn't have to do this," I'd said, gesturing all around the room.

"I know," she'd smiled. "I wanted to do something nice for you, though. I know you've been stressed out lately, with your boss being an acehole."

"A what?" I thought I'd misheard her.

"Yeah, you know. An acehole," she'd laughed, like *Who doesn't know what that is?*

"Ah, the infamous acehole," I'd said, mock-seriously. "The most terrifying of all holes."

That was back when Camila didn't swear. She'd used words like, "funk," "shizz," and "hale," in place of their profane counterparts. Now that she curses, I find that I miss her goofy words. It scares me to think that maybe I can only appreciate things in retrospect.

"Anyway, you acehole, I also ordered a case of Sonoran White Chocolate for you. It's in the fridge. I know you're always complaining about how no one sells it around here so I ordered it from a store in Phoenix."

"What did I do to deserve this?" I'd asked, incredulously. It wasn't necessarily a rhetorical question. I felt wildly unworthy of such thoughtful gestures.

"There's also a jar of Blueberry Kush under your pillow."

"Where the fuck were you when I was losing my baby teeth?" I'd smiled.

Camila had shrugged, smirking. I pulled her into my arms and kissed her.

"I love you," I'd blurted out. It was the first time either one of us had said those treacherous words. I remember thinking that her big brown eyes looked like black holes I wanted to fall into.

"I love you, too," she'd said, standing on her tiptoes to kiss me. And that was that. We'd said it. It was out in the universe. We couldn't take it back.

I'd wanted to ask Camila how'd she afforded to curate all the necessities for my dream world, how she hadn't been fired for skipping a week of work, but frankly, I didn't care. I was stoked that she not only accepted me for who I am, but actually encouraged my habits and interests. She did it to make me happy, and I was. Until I wasn't.

Shortly after we'd dropped the L bomb, she'd begun claiming my favorite director, Terrence Malick, as her own. There'd been an article about him in the Wall Street Journal. I didn't have access to the website, so I asked Camila to work her magic. She sent an email to her boss, who she knew subscribed to the newspaper, begging him for his login information. I know this because she'd blind copied me on the email.

"Arnold, do you mind giving me access to the Wall Street Journal? There's a recent article about my favorite director that I'd love to read."

Her favorite director. The fucking audacity. On the one hand, it seemed such a tiny indiscretion, but it made my blood boil. Why couldn't she have just said that her boyfriend was a huge Malick fan? The only exposure she'd had to his films was kissing my neck and rubbing my thigh on the couch while I furiously scribbled notes on camera angles, depth of field, and soft focus. But oh well, I loved her, didn't I? And that's what was important.

After stealing my interests, she began adopting my behaviors. I know this is going to sound a little weird, but I love bothering animals. Pets, not wild animals. I consider myself to be the resident pet-botherer of any household I'm in. I don't actually want the dog or cat or iguana to be irritated with me—I just want their undivided attention. Typically I'll do something like pet them aggressively or stick my toes in their noses when they either fall asleep or begin attending to anything that isn't me. Don't ask me why I find such joy in this, but I do. And to some extent

I think the pets do too. I say this because they moan and hiss and pretend to be infuriated, but when I get up to refill my drink or go to the bathroom they often follow me or at the very least, look at me with longing eyes.

After our third date, I'd invited Camila to a party at my ex-boyfriend's house. His name is Warren and he still can't decide if he hates me or wants us to be friends, which is inconsequential—his house is baller and my best friend, Sonya, was going to be there. She has auburn dreads and does heroin whenever she's menstruating. She hates her father and has a tattoo of him on her left bicep—I think some sort of power play on her part—and she believes that we are all living in a simulation created by a species so advanced we can't even fathom their intelligence. We know everything there is to know about each other. I love that she knows exactly who she is. Whether anyone's watching or not. I don't know what I'd do without her. Sonya is like my fortune teller, therapist, and financial advisor rolled into one.

Warren has a wiener dog named Brutus, with whom I've always been pretty chummy. Upon arriving to the party, I'd swept Brutus into my arms, holding him on his back like a baby even though I know it's not great for his spine, but he looked so adorable in that position, I could never help myself.

Throughout the evening I'd continued to terrorize Brutus, grabbing his snout, playing with his floppy ears, and chasing him into different rooms and yelling things like, "Why'd you have to kill Caesar?" and "From the statues I've seen, you were kinda hot." By the end of the night, Camila had usurped my throne as pet-botherer and was listing all of the foods Brutus resembles while trying to wrestle him into a Portland Trail Blazers t-shirt. Again, it was such a minor thing in the grand scheme of life that I hadn't spoken up. Not to Camila anyway. Naturally I pulled Sonya aside and complained about how that was my thing—not Camila's. Like a third-grader who thinks he invented dodgeball or freeze tag.

"You're being ridiculous. She's just trying to get close to you. It's actually kind of cute," Sonya had said, blowing me an air kiss.

"I guess you're right. Maybe I'm overreacting."

And it went that way for a while. A little something here, a little something there. A too-familiar facial expression, an uncomfortably-similar gesture, an uneasy feeling that my life was about to run away from me. Yet, I was powerless to stop it.

Now I've forgotten who she was when we met. She'd been a vegetarian, hadn't she? Hadn't she? She'd volunteered at a non-profit, maybe? Something to do with kids. I think she was pretty damn good at the piano, or had it been the guitar? She has three sisters, no, two brothers and one sister, or is she an only child? Didn't she love Sauvignon Blanc, or was she more of a rosé girl? Fuck, I don't know anymore. I think myself dizzy sometimes trying to recall the former Camila.

It's like that version of her had never existed to begin with. At least not without me. I never wanted this, I swear.

I wake to the sound of her light, rhythmic snoring. I'd been dreaming of a Dalmatian puppy rolling around in a yogurt-filled baby pool. It is likely that she's having the exact same dream, which I resent—there is hardly anything left that is solely mine. I roll over and examine her through crusted-over eyes. She looks like a burrito wrapped tightly in two blankets, which is conveniently the only position that I can fall asleep in. When she first started sleeping over I'd had to make a late-night trip to Walmart to buy more LaCrosse goose down blankets so she'd stop ripping the covers from me in the middle of the night, dismantling my burrito and leaving me to lie awake for hours.

Camila grunts, then rolls onto her side, facing me, her eyes still closed. The holes in her ears that had held dangling turquoise earrings only a week ago are now closed up. Having had my ear pierced during my self-proclaimed cool era in college, I know how these things work. I could probably still get an earring halfway through my ear, if I wanted.

I run my hand through her mahogany hair, which is messier and shorter than I remember, and I notice several blonde streaks that hadn't been there the night before. The exact same shade as my unkempt mop. I suppose she could have had a hair appointment I hadn't known about. Sure, let's be reasonable here. Let's list all the rational explanations before we jump to supernatural conclusions.

Dye job.

The sun.

She took a shower with Sunny D.

Some bees made honey on her head.

She is really Tonks from Harry Potter, and wanted to try out a new look.

An alien abducted her during the night and demanded she allow the alien to practice hair-styling techniques.

Okay, maybe not quite all rational conclusions, but I do think an alien abduction or secret witch identity is far more reasonable than her DNA suddenly replicating mine.

I can't ignore it anymore. Her once soft, round face has hardened, become more square and prominent like mine. Like someone had used a chisel to sharpen her jaw overnight. Her nose appears to have changed as well. It has elongated and narrowed, become more Nordic, more opportune for skiing. And her complexion—I swear that her skin is lighter than it was a few months ago. Give her a few more weeks and she'll fit right in at one of our Koskinen family reunions, her pale skin lathered in a thick layer of Coppertone 50 SPF sunscreen.

My heart is quivering in my chest, like a kitten brought inside from the freezing rain.

There's got to be a logical explanation for this. She could have been going to a tanning bed when we first met. Perhaps she'd recently gone on vacation—I'm thinking Maui or Cabo. I could chalk her increasing level of pallor up to the lack of sunlight in Portland. Everyone gets a little ghostly (and seasonally depressed) here—maybe it's the colors she's wearing. Dark shades can really wash a person's face out. That's more or less what Sonya says whenever I wear my black Jimi Hendrix t-shirt, except she phrases it, "You look like a fucking ghost, you twat."

I don't know what my next move is, but I can't ignore Camila's metamorphosis any longer.

Either I'm trapped in one of those straight-to-film sci-fi movies or I need to be checked into a mental hospital. Do I break up with her? Turn her over to the government? Hold a séance for the parts of Camila that have died? It's not like I started dating her for her pie-shaped face or her melanin. But any way you slice it, this is creepy. Maybe she's one of Frankenstein's science experiments gone terribly wrong, and thus was released into the wild, only to stumble into Norm's, the dive bar down the street, where she would promptly march up to me and ask me what I like least about myself—a question that had caught me off guard.

"Hi, you little monster," I whisper, brushing her hair away from her face. Joking about it makes it more bearable.

The problem is, in spite of all the twinning going on, I find her wildly appealing. Does this make me a narcissist? I don't know which is more disconcerting: her transformation or my pathological self-love.

Camila slowly opens her eyes. For the first time I realize that the room smells like sex. Last night when we fucked with just the salt lamp on, she'd looked enough like me that it had felt like I was masturbating in the mirror, only way better. When I removed her shirt, I felt around on her chest for a while, confused. I thought maybe I'd drank too much and had stumbled to an ex-boyfriend's house or something. Nothing was filling out her Victoria's Secret black lace bra. Her boobs had shrunken into muscular pecs that resembled mine. Don't get me wrong, I love pecs—I just wasn't expecting to find them on her.

"Morning, baby," Camila whispers, her voice raspy from sleep, and, well, from becoming a man.

"Hey, you," I say. No matter how frustrated and spooked I am, I can't make myself be anything but sweet to her. It would be like breaking my own nose. Plus, she's got a good heart, and I am in love with her, right?

She cuddles up to me, burying her face in my chest, and I wrap my arms around her shoulders.

"You know what my first thought was when I woke up and saw you?" she asks.

"What?"

"Just how I feel so close to you. You make me feel safe, like you're my lover and my brother."

I can feel her smiling against my chest. I don't have it in me to break her heart. She means well, she really does.

"Huh," I say, non-committal.

"Oh, you know what I mean. Not in like a creepy, tiptoe down to your bedroom, careful not to wake Mom and Dad way. Although, we could role-play that, if you're down," Camila laughs, and I laugh too, in spite of myself. It's a joke I would make.

"What I'm trying to say is that I think what we have is special. I never met any men like you back in Venezuela. They were all so closed-off, so uncomfortable with their sexuality. I like how fluid you are."

I nod, staring at the cracks in the ceiling for a few moments.

"Camila, would you mind, uh, going to look in the mirror real quick?" I ask, trying to sound casual. Nothing is as chivalrous as insisting your girlfriend examine herself the moment she wakes up.

"Why? Do I have a booger? Is there something in my teeth?"

She covers her mouth with her palm. I grab her hand and gently remove it.

"No, nothing like that. Would you please just go look?"

"Okay, weirdo," she says, giving me a quick kiss, then jumping out of bed to run to the bathroom.

I never thought time could creep so slowly as when she's in the bathroom, allegedly scrutinizing her reflection. I try to prepare for every possible outcome. She hasn't screamed yet, which means she's not surprised or terrified. Maybe she's been noticing the changes too and didn't know how to bring it up. That would be understandable. After all, it's not like asking your partner if he or she or they would like to go to a Kid Rock concert with you—as painful as that experience sounds. She may return crying, so I'll hold her and comfort her and tell her that I love her no matter what. She may be flustered or confused, not willing to believe the unbelievable. I don't know what I'll do then. Perhaps we will find solidarity in our bewilderment.

I never thought time could creep so slowly as when she's in the bathroom, allegedly scrutinizing her reflection.

Camila arrives in the bedroom doorway rubbing her eyes.

"I don't understand what you wanted me to see. I mean, the bags under my eyes aren't looking so hot, but that's it."

I stare at her in disbelief. Sure, there are some dark half-moons under her eyes, but those are the least of my concerns. Hell, they're not even on the list.

"What?" she probes.

"You don't notice any, uh, changes?"

"No, babe. Have I gained weight or something? Maybe it's the beer. No, you know what, I read that it's a myth that beer makes you fat. And light beer isn't always the best option either. Sometimes the stouts or porters actually have the lowest calories. Wait, so what's the problem?"

"I—I don't know. I really don't. I was certain you'd see it. Fuck, am I going crazy? Like not in the colloquial way, but in the real way."

I press on the skin below my eyes feeling for bulging bags. Yep, they're there. Great. I can now operate under the notion that I never need to look in the mirror again, now that I have my own living, breathing, loving human mirror.

I'm on the verge of having a panic attack when Camila climbs on top of me and nibbles on my earlobe, and I can feel myself getting hard despite my turmoil. She feels it too. She runs her tongue slowly down my neck and just as I start to moan, she pulls back and smirks at me.

"Our sex last night was really good, wasn't it," she says, not really asking.

"Yeah, it was," I whisper as she reaches her hand down my lime green boxer briefs. "It was like you knew what I wanted before I did," I breathe. And it's true. Every desire I had was fulfilled before I could conceptualize the shape of the desire itself.

"That's how you know we're a great fucking match, Jerome."

I wince at her profanity. It sounds wrong coming out of her mouth, like she's a robot that has been programmed to imitate a human. But I don't mention her sudden change in vernacular. My dick is throbbing in her hand. She peels my boxer briefs off and I temporarily forget (or dismiss?) the problem at hand.

"What's this scar from?" Camila asks, tracing the barely-detectable line dividing my chest in half. We've just arrived to Wahclella Falls after hiking for about forty minutes. She's wearing a gold bandana that holds back the short blonde hairs around her face and a blue tank top that shows off her ever-growing biceps. I'm shocked she even noticed my scar. I've been diligent with my vitamin E oil application for the past twelve years. No one ever points it out.

"I had open-heart surgery as a kid," I say, looking into her now-gray eyes. The 350-foot waterfall thrashes behind her.

"It's beautiful," she says. "Is your heart okay now?"

"Yeah, thankfully I haven't had any problems since."

No one has ever told me my scar was beautiful before, except for maybe my mom. I'd been bullied to no avail as a kid. They said I was weak like my heart. In order to compensate, I began lifting weights incessantly, a habit I've maintained into adulthood.

"I can feel that you're self-conscious about it. There's no need to be," says Camila. This isn't the first time she's said something like this. Lately it's been, I can feel your sadness. I can feel your anxiety. I can feel your pleasure. It's like we are sharing the same amygdala now. I want to chop mine out and fry it up in a pan with butter and spices. Anything to separate myself from her.

"I used to invent stories about what really happened. My favorite involved my having a near-death experience. So, it was like the 1700s. Basically a time when the doctors knew nothing more about medicine than your average toddler does today. I'd been struck by lightning and my heart had temporarily stopped. The doctors had deemed me dead and began performing an autopsy. I awoke on the table as they were slicing my chest open. Crazy shit. The timid doctor died instantaneously of shock and the other ran away, wailing and ripping out chunks of his hair. I sewed myself up and made it home in time for a nice steak dinner," I say.

She laughs in a good-natured way and thanks me for telling her something so personal about me. I brush it off like it's no big deal, but I don't know why I continue to feed parts of myself to her, knowing everything I say and do is a blueprint for her life.

"You know what? I've always been jealous of people with scars," Camila says, peeling off her shorts and tank top to reveal a white bikini with orange and red flowers on it.

"Why's that?" I ask, slipping out of my shorts.

"There's always a story behind a scar. It's like collecting memories from your past and decorating your body with them."

"You don't have any scars?"

"Nope, not even from falling down and scraping my knee as a kid or something silly like that. Not one."

She holds up her hands, palms facing the sky, as if to say, Oh well.

"So in a way, you have no past," I say. I mean for it to sound like a joke, but I think she can tell that I mean it. She squints into the sun then looks at me with empty eyes. They look dead, despite the shimmering sun.

She doesn't respond. We wade into the water, which is so cold a tingle shoots up my spine. We swim for a while in silence. Then she stops swimming and calls to me from across the lake and says, "I can feel your fear."

I make a mental note to text Sonya, "SOS."

I'm nibbling on pretzels at Norm's, and talking to Sonya, who has helped me through dozens of failed relationships, including that time I found out my boyfriend was a secret white supremacist.

"You know why all of your past relationships have failed right?" she asks, tilting her head the way she does when she wants to call me an imbecile but understands I need love.

"Not really," I shrug, taking a sip of my PBR. Several times I've tried to convince a buddy of mine who works at Norm's to order a keg of Sonoran White Chocolate Ale, but he usually just grins at me like, Do you know that we're a dive bar and not just any dive bar but the worst dive bar imaginable?

"Well, allow me to enlighten you—"

"Wait, how long have you known the secret to my dating life and not told me?" I interject.

"You're not exactly the most receptive person I know, Jerome. I love you, but I didn't know how you'd handle something like that. I thought maybe you'd eventually figure it out on your own, but I guess I'm gonna have to spoon-feed it to you," she says, scratching her neck and nodding to the bartender for another round.

"Please."

"For one reason or another it seems like you want everyone you date to be more like you and less like them. Which is confusing, 'cause like why not just date yourself then, you know? Basically, I've decided that you don't want to be alone but you don't want to compromise either, which is tricky. Like take Janessa for example. She went to Yoga Teacher school or whatever you call it to get certified, and then you convinced her that all that stuff is bogus and that she should be the lead in one of your short films that you never edit or do anything with."

"What the fuck," I say.

"I'm not done. Then there was Alex, who was smokin' hot by the way. He was a stud snowboarder, but you hate the snow so you never went to his competitions, constantly bitching about how he should pick a more accessible passion, or something. Do you see what I'm saying here? There's a trend. You don't appreciate your partners' quirks, interests, idiosyncrasies, their very themness. If you wanna know what I think, which I'm assuming you do because otherwise you wouldn't be here, I think that you didn't want to put forth the effort it took to truly know and appreciate someone. That's exhausting, and sometimes even disheartening. The more you learn about someone the more you run the risk of hating them. Tell me I'm wrong. And I know you didn't want to hate your partners. You just wished they'd known the difference between a continuity cut and match cut in film. Or that they'd understand your obsession with cinéma vérité, that stupid French film movement you're always carrying on about. Or that they wouldn't nag you for smoking so much Blueberry Kush. That's all," Sonya shrugs.

I don't know what to say. I've never had anyone lay it out like that for me. The way she explains it, I sound like a total douchebag. And maybe I am. Maybe Camila's transformation is all my fault.

"So, do you think I like, willed this into existence?" I ask.

"Could you be any more vague? Willed what into existence?"

"For fuck's sake. You know what I'm talking about. Do I really have to say it again? Camila is basically mutating before my eyes. She looks like me, sounds like me, shares all of my same interests, passions, likes, and dislikes."

"Guess you finally are dating yourself. I've gotta see this," Sonya grins, taking a sip of her Modelo.

"No way, no fucking way. Not while I'm in this vulnerable state. I'll shit myself."

"Okay, well at least take some photos to track her progress."

"That's not a bad idea. What else you got?" I ask.

"Well, have you considered talking to her about it? I'm just spitballing here, but maybe be a mature adult?" she says, tilting her head down and raising her eyebrows.

"I did tell her to look in the mirror the other day, but she didn't note anything out of the ordinary. I'm starting to think I'm imagining the whole thing."

"You have to be more direct than that. It's not fair to expect her to pick up on something," she says, pursing her lips.

"What would I even say?"

"There's not exactly a handbook for these types of things. Maybe ask her if she's noticed anything off lately or if she's been going through any major changes."

"So much for direct. That sounds like I'm suggesting she has early onset menopause, Sonya. You can do better than that," I laugh.

"How about you tell her how you feel? Like an expressive, sensitive man. You can practice on me. Ready, go," she says.

"Okay, Camila. Um, I love you. You're really, really great. You even had that threesome with Marc and I last week, which I appreciate—I promise I do—but, um, I feel like you're gradually transforming into me," I stutter.

"Cut out the preamble. Unrelated: how was the threesome?"

"Shhhh, I'll tell you some other time when my life isn't in shambles."

Sonya makes a big production out of rolling her eyes, then finishes off her Modelo, beckoning for another one.

"I forgot what a drama queen you can be. Your life isn't in shambles. If anything, hers is."

"How so?"

"Hello, she's losing her identity, Jerome. She's become a chameleon."

I nod. I know it's a common misconception that the reason chameleons change colors is to camouflage themselves, but I can't help but think this chameleon is unique.

After my talk with Sonya, I begin taking pictures of Camila while she's sleeping and documenting her metamorphosis. I obsess over every miniscule detail, but not once do I mention her changes. I'm afraid she'll have the same response as last time: I don't notice anything different.

About a week and a half later, Camila and I are sitting on the gray Lanza loveseat in the living room one morning. Camila is nearly bursting out of her white Nordstrom nightgown. I pretend not to notice. She's reading The Film Book: A Complete Guide to the World of Film while I play Bioshock on Xbox. I can feel the warmth of her gaze while I shoot a crazed splicer then use telekinesis to hurl his corpse at a living splicer. Once I die, I groan loudly and chuck the controller onto the antique oak chest we use as a coffee table. I glance at Camila and she feigns a cheery smile. There's something terribly wrong with her smile. Her teeth are too white, too straight—the teeth of someone who hasn't lived at all. It's as if her mouth is erasing any memory of her so that it can begin again from scratch. It won't be long before my slight overbite miraculously materializes in her mouth.

Infected by a rare strain of courage, I put my hand on her thigh and ask, "Are you feeling okay?"

"Yeah, of course. Why? Do I look sick?" Camila asks, scooching closer to me.

"No, uh, not exactly."

I can feel my body tense up, but there's nothing I can do about it. I've always been a terrible liar. I clam up, stain my shirts, accidentally shatter glasses.

"Then what is it, babe?"

I pause, trying to encourage the courage to spread, but my white cells attack it and it dies before it can reach my mouth.

"Nothing. I'm just checking in. Seeing how you're doing. I realized I don't ask you that enough. I mean, in the real way—not just the 'How you doin?' way."

She leans in and gives me a slow kiss on the mouth. Her tongue tastes like coffee and peppermint toothpaste. Kissing her on this couch reminds me of our first date. I'd sat as far away from her as possible because I was nervous and I never make the first move. She'd inched closer to me until she was practically in my lap and then kissed me. Her lips had felt like they'd been recently sanded—soft and satisfying. After a few minutes of making out, she'd led me by the hand to my bedroom as if it were hers and always had been.

"You're so sweet," she says, once she pulls away. "I was actually gonna ask you the same thing. You've been acting kinda funny lately."

"What do you mean?"

"Like, you practically leapt out of bed this morning when I put my hand on your chest. That wasn't exactly the reaction I'd been going for," she trails off, obviously hurt.

"Oh, that was nothing. Your hand was just freezing. That was all. And I really had to go to the bathroom."

I don't know how to tell her that I'd been shocked by her hairy, vascular hand. Although, frankly, I don't know why I'm surprised by anything at this point. Shame on me.

"But you didn't go to the bathroom when you left the room."

"Yeah, I did. You just don't remember. It was early."

She lets her cheery mask down just for a second and I catch a glimpse of her eyes. They look vacant and expressionless. Like someone had turned the lights on in what they believed to be an occupied house only to discover that it had been abandoned decades earlier. But she catches herself.

"You know what you need to feel better?" Camila says, even though I hadn't admitted anything was wrong. "You need a good breakfast and a mimosa."

She stands up and practically skips into the kitchen. I follow her, without making the conscious decision to do so. It seems that I'm too scared to think or make decisions for myself. While she digs through the cabinets for suitable pans, I examine the Angel Falls postcard she'd recently hung up on the fridge using a Portland magnet. The postcard is from her father but the handwriting looks unnervingly similar to hers. A wave of icy fear rushes through my bloodstream. I have to fight the sudden urge to buy a one-way ticket to Venezuela, to drop in on her family unexpectedly. I want to see it with my own eyes that they exist. That she'd come from somewhere other than my imagination.

She pops a bottle of champagne and makes me a mimosa, humming a song I wrote with my high school band, Raven Meat.

"Let's see if this will help your head," she smiles.

"Thanks," I mumble, grabbing the champagne flute from her hand.

> She lets her cheery mask down just for a second and I catch a glimpse of her eyes. They look vacant and expressionless.

Camila watches me drink my mimosa with wild intensity. It is as if she can't fathom a world in which I am not hers. She looks like a wolf preparing to howl at the tumescent moon. It feels like my body is one large exposed nerve, like a patient in the game Operation. My insides are buzzing. I finish the mimosa and hold the flute out for her to refill it, which she does. I chug two more right in a row, which Camila replenishes before I can ask, looking anywhere but at her.

"Wait, no. No, no, no. Don't tell me that's a scar on your chest," I say, once my eyes focus on her. I can detect the hint of a small scar over her sternum, peeking out from the top of her nightgown. She tilts her chin down and smiles at the discolored skin then looks back up at me, proud.

"Yeah, I've had it for years. I used to be embarrassed of it, but now I embrace it. It's empowering to know that I can accept every part of me. You know what I mean?" she asks, as if we are having a normal conversation and this is a normal world and we are a normal couple.

"I think you've gone batshit crazy, woman," I blurt out without thinking.

"What was that?" Camila threatens, her smile malicious.

I clear my throat and hold my flute out for another refill. She examines the glass in my hand as if it's an alien object, then looks back up at me.

"Nothing, okay. I'm sorry. I don't know why I said that. I think all the stress at work is really getting to me," I submit.

She takes the flute and pours me another mimosa, then hands it back to me. She bites her bottom lip a little and stares up at me with those dead eyes again. I feel like her prey, absolutely helpless and afraid.

I want to tell you that her transformation has reversed itself, that everything is going swimmingly, but like I said, I'm a horrendous liar.

Camila puts herself to bed early one evening after having played a daytime Californication drinking game in which we took a shot every time Hank Moody fucked a girl or pissed off his soulmate, Karen. I take this time to retrieve a folder from the bone-white, Ikea desk in the corner of our bedroom. I open the manila file folder to the most recent page, dated yesterday. As all of the pages do, it contains a photo I took of her while she was sleeping and any mention of new interests or likes or dislikes that align with mine (most recently: She always always always wanted to grow up to be Bender from The Breakfast Club.)

I tiptoe to the edge of the bed. My hand trembles as I hold the photo next to her cheek. I can see the blood moving through my hand like watercolor.

I'm afraid of what I'll discover this time.

There's a new mole on her chin that hadn't been there yesterday. I've always hated having that mole. One single, thick black hair continues to grow from it, no matter how many times I pluck it. She'll encounter the same problem soon enough. A wicked part of me is enjoying her suffering as she receives the unattractive traits from me. You don't get to pick and choose, you crazy witch.

I look from her face to the photo and back again a few times in a twisted version of one of those bar games in which you have to spot the difference between the two images. I don't notice anything besides the mole, so I return the photo to its rightful place and set the folder down on the desk, holding onto the edge for support. No matter how many times I do this, I never get used to the anxiety that comes along with making new discoveries. I take a few deep breaths to calm down, but my heart continues to do the Harlem Shake. I am not convinced that the oxygen I've inhaled hasn't flowed into her lungs instead.

Once my legs feel steady enough to walk, I grab my camera from bottom drawer of the desk then crouch down on the floor, careful not to step on the 90's videotapes strewn about, and take a few pictures of her half-smiling sleep face that I will print later and add to the progress reports. I return everything to its rightful place and slouch down on the floor against the wall and begin to cry.

A fire has started inside my life and I can't "Stop, Drop, and Roll." Instead, I sit and watch the flames dance, brilliant in their cruelty. It's not like they teach you how to deal with this shit in school. Never once did a teacher hand out a worksheet on what to do if your partner begins to transform into you. But, according to Sonya, this is what I wanted, wasn't it?

Less friction, fewer disagreements. A lover to mirror my heart.

I'm nibbling on pretzels again at Norm's, waiting for Sonya to meet me. I'm working on my eighth Upheaval IPA. I needed something stronger than the usual PBR. She arrives after a few minutes, sits down on the stool next to me, and straightens her posture, like Let's get down to business.

"Did you bring the pictures?" she asks.

"Of course I brought the fucking pictures," I say, pulling five out of my back pocket. I lay them on the bar top and order them chronologically.

Sonya fingers them delicately, her brow furrowed. She studies them for a while then looks up at me, her eyes wide.

"This is some Twilight Zone shit. I'm not gonna lie. When you first told me, I thought you were insane, but this is really happening."

"Thank you."

"How can this be? I mean, what kind of sorcery is this?"

"I don't know, Sonya. You said it, though, didn't you? I wanted this. I reject anyone who isn't me."

"I thought I was exaggerating."

"Well."

We sit in silence for a while, processing. I finish my beer and order another one. It's all that I can think to do.

"Okay, listen to me, Jerome. I'm gonna give it to you straight. You need to tell homegirl what's up or else I'm coming over there and slapping some sense into her," she says.

"No offense, but I don't think sense is what she's missing."

"Oh shut up. You know what I mean. This has gone on long enough."

"You act like I'm a kid who's been pulling a girl's hair to get her attention in class. I'm not in control of this, Sonya. Can't you see? She has this way about her. She can flip a switch in a second. A switch that should only appear in a Hitchcock film," I say.

"I hear you, but you need your life back. And the only way you're gonna get it is to grow some ovaries and tell her what's what."

"Alright, but it's your fault when the cops never find my body."

Sonya rolls her eyes like she does, then orders us another round. I'm trashed by the time I hug her goodbye.

Camila is reading The Sun Also Rises outside on the porch when I get home. I've read that book so many times, I can recite it forward and backward. I stumble up the four stairs leading from the lawn to our porch and sit down beside her.

"How was hanging out with Sonya?" Camila asks, looking up from her book.

"Pretty good. You know, same old shit. Just shot some pool and drank some beers." And talked about how you might be worse than Norman Bates.

> Camila is reading The Sun Also Rises outside on the porch when I get home. I've read that book so many times, I can recite it forward and backward.

"Good, that sounds nice," she smiles that cheery smile, reminiscent of The Stepford Wives, that makes me want to gauge her eyes out.

"What do you think of that book?" I slur.

"I absolutely love it—how aimless they all are. It makes sense that Gertrude Stein called them the Lost Generation. Lady Brett Ashley is such a progressive character for that time, too. Short hair, sleeps around, drinks like a lush. Girl can get it. And Jake, I feel so bad for him. It's depressing, but in a delicious way."

"Of course you fucking love it. That is my exact review of that book. Word. For. Word. I wish just once—just once—that you'd disagree with me about something. It could be anything for all I care. If it's sunny out, tell me that it's rainy. I don't give a shit. Just have your own god damn opinion."

I exhale deeply and slump back into my seat like a newspaper-stuffed scarecrow.

"You're drunk, Jerome," she hisses through clenched teeth.

"So?" I shout, raising my eyebrows. The flock of crows sitting on our fence squawks in response. Camila regains her composure and softens her voice.

"So you've never mentioned this book before. How would I be able to copy you?"

She's got me there. My neurons aren't firing as quickly as they usually do.

"Well, I own it, don't I?" I don't stick my tongue out, but the way I say it, I might as well have.

"You could have bought it and never read it or had it gifted to you," she says.

"Alright, so I'm drunk. How about I go to bed and sober up and while I'm at it, you can stop becoming me," I scream. I've tapped into a primal part of my psyche. I feel wild and free and it feels fucking good.

"What the hell are you talking about?" Camila asks, her mask slipping. The dead eyes are coming out to play.

"I tried to tell you, Camila. I really tried. I told you to look in the mirror, but you refused to admit what you saw. I don't know if you're a victim in all this too or if you're the evil one behind it all, but let me tell you, your skin is as pale as my Finnish ass. There, I said it. And you know what else? Your hair is short and blonde and your tits have been replaced by pecs. You have a scar down your chest like I do that you claim has always been there."

Camila doesn't respond. She stands up from her seat and I think she's going to punch me, but then she falls to her knees and begins to writhe in pain. Her body contorts and her bones crack then grow longer and snap back into place. She's wailing like a banshee. I don't move or try to help her. I think a part of me hopes that she is dying, that this is the end of her. I hate myself for hoping that. While I'm scolding myself for wishing death upon another person, she stands up calmly and points at me to stand up. I do, and now we are eye to eye. She's grown to 6 ft. 3 in. right before me.

"Did you say something?" Camila asks, returning to her seat and her book and the rest of her life.

I pass out before I can speak.

Months later when I get home from work, Camila is building a bookshelf, a beer sitting on the floor next to her. I bend down and give her a kiss then go change into more comfortable clothes.

When I return to the living room, Camila stops what she's doing and runs into my arms. It's hard for me to catch her since she's now pushing 220 lbs.

"I missed you all day," she says.

"I missed you too. I was thinking we could go out on a date tonight. Get some crab legs and steak. It's been a while since we've been out on a proper date," I say, smiling a close-mouthed smile.

"Sounds perfect. I'll go take a shower and get changed," she says.

Later when we arrive at the restaurant, a few beers deep, the hostess grins and says that she, too, is a twin before leading us to our seats.

"What?" Camila mouths incredulously to me, before taking a seat.

I smile politely at the waitress, thanking her, and sit down. Jazz music plays softly in the background. We both order the king crab legs and whatever IPA they have, then I excuse myself to go to the bathroom.

As I wash my hands, I examine my face in the mirror. It's a good-looking face, I decide, slapping my cheeks a few times. Without thinking, I lean over the sink and give myself a long kiss, the glass cold against my lips. I don't move, not even when an old man enters the bathroom and coughs loudly.

I imagine I am in a movie, and I am waiting for the director to yell "Cut!"

INSIDE THESE BLANCH YELLOW WALLS

ANDREW LAFLECHE

not quite nicotine stained
only the colour now faded
from when they were painted
forty years ago

atop worn tiled stairs
dotted with spilt red wine
i climb each night after dark
with my glass

maybe i should go to bed
at least the thought manifests
briefly, before pouring another
in my apartment

music turned low or off
to hear the wind outside strike
the drafty single pane windows
all four of them

lips chapped crusted purple
face worn like an old mitt
maybe i should slow down
or keep going

one month, two months
three months since she left
and each first i tell myself
time to shape up

it's the ninth this morning
or the night of the eighth

depending how days are counted
thursday still

refill the cabernet glass
watch the legs spider down
in the translucent shadow
of a tear's heartbeat

if only she could see me now
right? lose my shit tomorrow
today is no day to fall apart
begin again

that's how progress is made
get to work, keep working
don't stop till the job is done
the bottle is empty

continue with gin that is dry
junipers are less contemptuous
or so i was told once before
believe what anymore?

fall asleep cigarette in hand
wake up with a burn under lip
and a hole in the carpet
disappointed

not for the deposit
the face i can't shave
the litre and a half of wine   .
or the liquor

disappointed i woke at all

feeling worse than shame

survive the day and do it again

inside these blanch yellow walls

CLAIRVIUS NARCISSE

KEN FARRELL

I think I am
being stalked by the man
I could be.
Late at night, he murmurs
through my window
his plan for the coming day.
He is my severed shadow
freed of the soul-binding sinew
his greatest pleasure
taking the measure of me
and before dawn
he slips my shoes on
prances through my home
a happy genius pirouetting
over the spotty rug.

I wake and struggle
against the lesser in me
but lie dumb, a tangle
of nerves, grave-sewn
though I live, as he
loves my wife more lovingly.
Is he the phantom,
or is it me? Am I
who he labors to master,
zombie to his bokor?
No, I am not
the newly raised undead
soon to be enslaved
but the un-needed, the never born.

I am just the unripe twin
bulging in his skull
blob of plasma   web of dead-end
nerves   scattering
of teeth   a teary   twitchy
albino eye   I am merely a cyst
he longs to excise
to ease the throb
to put me down
once
          and for all

ADEPT

KEN FARRELL

Waygate eyes say
the middle seat is hers,
her smile, a deft athame.
Tortoise shell: is that
what her glasses are called,
this girl next to me on the plane?
Her end-flipped, short black hair:
topiaried?... a dozen ravens
effusing from a shadowy cloud.
I know nothing of people, how people
meet or talk. Here is someone
I would like to meet over and again,
but with what words to begin?
Do I tell her I find trees dubious
...or ask her how je te dis
"merde" makes sense?
Should my tongue conjure a word,
the first in a language uttered just for us?
If I don't speak,
where will I find her?
Her shaker-shingled cottage
waits in an aspen hollow outside town
brightened by skylights and filled
with books, her long brown blazer
laid across a chairback
and not a cat in sight.
She is gone too much for such
an entanglement, hang-gliding
over the astral plane, gathering
Yōkai in Aokigahara,
or on a deep-sea survey where she discovers
a fish that subsists on inert dreams
and now it bears her name.

What is her name?
Am I dreaming her, this girl
next to me on the plane?...this piper of souls
with tourmaline and turquoise
oval-stoned rings hugging
each long finger, this be-birded sorceress
flashing a black-stoned tongue-ring
hiding many so wonderful secrets.

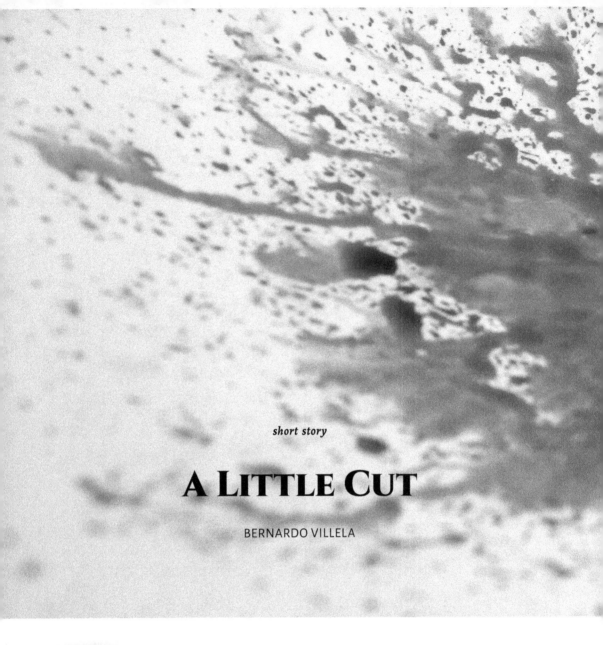

short story

A Little Cut

BERNARDO VILLELA

1 *t was just a little cut*, he said to calm his hypochondriac mind.

At least that's what he tried to tell himself. It was the kind of thing that had been easy to believe for a while even if it wasn't entirely true.

The knife had accidentally stabbed him about a half inch below his left ring finger, on the meaty part of his hand. It had been a deep cut.

It's just a little cut, he told himself in between bursts of expletives and trying to stop the bleeding.

It wasn't little, it wasn't the end of the world, but it wasn't little. The wound was deep enough that it could have done with a few stitches. Because the cut was self-diagnosed as small, however, the cut would be dealt with by bandaids and antiseptic ointment for however long it'd take to heal.

It was a while. He lost count of the number of bandaids he ended up using. Healing took around a month.

The cut slowly filled in as layers of epidermis seemed to stitch themselves back together one-by-one. At last his hand was whole again. Only a small quarter-inch scar permanently marked the accident on his body.

At least it did yesterday, this morning he saw no scar on his left hand at all. He thought maybe it was a trick of the light or that he was just not yet fully awake. But all he knew was that his eyes told him it was gone.

When he awoke the following morning he checked his hand before taking a shower. No scar again. But the cut was back as if it had just occurred yesterday.

I was dreaming. I was hallucinating. What's the difference?

Those were the things he tried to convince himself of the next day. Being torn would not ease his mind. He had to choose.

Quel est la difference?

French, that was real life.

The cut was a hallucination. Decided.

Now, when is French? Is it today? Is it a school day? I'm sweating.

He looked at his alarm clock: 10:51 a.m. Tuesday.

Summer vacation. I cut my hand during the school year. It's summer. I'm hallucinating. I'm wasting my summer hallucinating a cut.

In a few simple steps he was close to reclaiming his life; closer to reality than he was before.

Though he was acting like a child, he was not. He was a high school teacher. English, now; social studies previously. He was wasting his vacation worrying about a cut. He had fleeting hours of sunlight left to enjoy now that he'd showered and eaten.

He'd go swimming, then by night he'd write. That's why he taught. It paid the bills and gave him time to try and get his writing in order. Not the most original plan in the world, but on occasion it even worked.

No more wasting the day, he'd forget the cut and go to the pool. But he wouldn't forget.

As soon as he got to the pool there was cause to remember:

NO SWIMMING PERMITTED UNDER THE FOLLOWING CONDITIONS

• Open wound(s)

I heard they're usually pretty sharp. That's what we pay dues for: qualified lifeguards. They'll see it.

He checked his left hand. The wound was now eye-shaped and half the circumference of a dime. As the cut was healing, sometimes he'd press the flesh of his palm and the gash would spread, forming the shape he now saw.

Don't make that face it'll freeze that way.

A parent's lie. Would it apply here as the truth? Had the cut frozen? A tiny cesspool of blood formed within the wound. Surely, he was not getting in. Something compelled him to try. Maybe it was just nerves. He was up next to sign-in. Maybe he wanted to dispel the notion that he was hallucinating.

He put on his sunglasses. It was one of the few tasks he did left-handed. He did it when the lifeguard at the sign-in table looked up, so he had to see it.

"How ya doing, Mr. Johnson?" the lifeguard who looked like a displaced surfer boy said.

He didn't see it.

How could he not see it?

Mr. Johnson signed in and moved on. He found a chair. Moving in slow motion he eventually tried taking a dip. The chlorinated water did not wash the hallucination away. He had the cut. It was larger now. There was blood in the water. He ran off.

He waited in the parking lot for fifteen minutes. Surely, they'd see the blood. Clear the pool. Clean it. Maybe even drain it.

The cut, now a hole, was the size of a quarter.

He got back home and considered going to the hospital.

What if the emergency room personnel don't see it? What if they do and the doctor doesn't? Even if I lie to get in, saying it's something internal, I'd still likely end up in a psych ward.

He needed to say something innocuous. His confusion was not helped by his hypochondria.

Brian! That's it!

He'd never believed in a twelve-step program until H.A. He had a sponsor for just this kind of situation. Brian would end it. How could he forget? Maybe there were dreams and hallucinations in his recollections.

He sent an ice-breaking text. He got a quick reply.

Good to hear from you. I take it you've done well. What's up?

Johnson replied instantly:

CRISIS!!!

Brian was engaged.

Walk through it. Baby steps. We got you through the cut.

The cut, yes, Brian knew about the cut. After he bandaged it up he'd called him.

That was the last time.

"Go to the hospital," Brian had told him. Johnson insisted he didn't want to.

"That's your fear of doctors."

"Isn't going to the hospital for this letting the hypochondria win?"

"No. You cut yourself. You just don't want to go because you think you'll get *really* sick there."

Johnson was not in the mood for a long debate tonight. He took a picture of the cut. He labeled it a crisis, but to a hypochondriac that could mean almost anything.

Does this look like something to you?

Which was shorthand for "Does this look like cancer or anything else life-threatening?"

His phone rang.

"Get to the hospital!" Brian said, eschewing formality.

"What? You see it?"

"I'm not blind. It's a chasm on your palm."

He could understand the lifeguard not seeing it. People can look right at you and not pay attention.

"I bled in the pool and no one saw it."

"What?" Brian, said sounding more dumbfounded than before.

"I thought I imagined it when the lifeguard saw nothing. But I bled in the pool, dripped blood on the deck and left, but there wasn't a scream, they didn't shut the pool down. How did they not see that?"

The line was quiet.

"I'm picking you up. Don't go on your own."

"OK."

"I'll be there in ten."

Brian hung up. Johnson looked at his left hand, the skin now blossoming away from his person in flaps that were—

Labial.

— tattered. His hand was not large but he saw the maw pulsing, red, and bleeding. It was baseball-sized.

On his right hand was a wrist watch. Johnson would be in his house in nine minutes.

The dread was now more real. It wasn't only his eyes that had seen it. As the rupture crawled from his palm to his fingers it became hard to breathe. He wasn't sure he could move if he wanted to. No one would get him help quicker than Brian could.

All his brain, in a shocked and addled state, was good for was regurgitating nonsense that seemed apropos to the scenario.

That song about a boa constrictor, then something by Lovecraft. What was it? Did it matter? His fingers were being peeled from the bottom up like grotesque bananas.

His flayed skin moved to the back of his hand. As opposed to most, Johnson didn't know that part of his hand that well.

Cool Air was the Lovecraft thing. Why'd he think of it?

Eight minutes.

Skin started to slough, then slither down the length of his arm. Before him he could see bone, musculature, tendons, and blood.

After a certain point it got to be as if it were happening to someone else, as if he were merely a spectator.

Is that the shock or had reality gotten fuzzy since the phone call? Is something more wrong with me than hypochondria? Something more dissociative?

As his skin popped over his elbow, splitting more, he saw that his funny bone wasn't so funny, something distracted him: all the capillaries in his fingers exploded.

And blood ran through the Dardanelles…

He didn't know what that meant, just that he was woozy.

The skin of his left shoulder came off as if ripped, tendons snapped, bones crunched.

Seven minutes.

He didn't know why he couldn't feel a thing.

The skin on his shoulder was being torn away in large chunks and then stopped. For a second that looked like the end of it. But then the virus, the entity, demon, vortex; whatever was skinning him, got back to it. Large sections of the skin on his back, like large sections of wallpaper whose glue had failed, slid off, pouring forth blood.

Shock, fear and adrenaline had seemed to have numbed him, but when his whole midsection began to spontaneously herniate that is when the screams began.

There were no more thoughts of being eaten alive, of *Cool Air*, or even that he'd see Brian; but as his body distended and burst; as his eyes popped from their sockets and separated from their optic nerves; as his eardrums burst irreparably; as several major blood vessels and arteries spontaneously ruptured simultaneously; with the onset of cardiac arrest; he knew there was no hope.

Thought ceased.

Adrenaline overridden, there was only pain.

And soon there was nothing and Johnson left the world, a man referred to by his last name, without understanding how or why that was.

Brian was due in a minute.

Brian actually arrived in two minutes having hit some slower-than-usual traffic. He was glad the door had not been locked, looking for a key would have cost him time he didn't have to spare.

As he got into Johnson's bedroom, he saw blood. Plenty of it. He saw his clothes. As for the body there were many fragments in the blood that could not be understood. Brian had no concept of what was going on.

When the police arrived the confusion he and they felt would grow by leaps and bounds.

"Sir, there's nothing wrong with his hand in this picture."

Brian was dumbfounded. He was about to protest, then thought better of it. He knew Johnson hadn't been murdered. He knew what he saw and what they'd believe.

"I know," he said calmly. "He was a hypochondriac. I was his sponsor."

"Like in A.A.?" The cop's partner said.

"Exactly. I…I broke a rule. I told him he was hurt because I couldn't help him over the phone. I wanted to come over. Check the rest of the message trail."

They did as he had given them his phone.

"So it took you exactly eleven minutes to arrive here?"

"I told him ten. It was eleven. I missed one light."

"Were you with someone?"

"My wife is waiting by the phone."

Nothing added up. The way the cops saw it if Brian killed Johnson then called them he'd have confessed by now. If someone else had come and killed him, even if you could explain the mess, how could you explain that there was no trace of an assailant? If it was suicide, where's the body? If he was this violently ill, whatever in Heaven or Hell could cause that kind of sickness, why did he think it was his hand?

And as for that body, if it was really here but in smithereens, how'd that happen?

Brian was not held, just told to stay in town as a person of interest.

A spatter expert came in. The police and forensics concluded that most of his brain tissue, blood, intestines and a lot of bone could be accounted for in the fragments they found.

"Blood in a pattern like this, with shards of brain, bone, and tendons. It's like a suicide bombing. But where's the explosion?"

There was neither a murder nor a suicide to put on record. Though those cops would never forget what they started to call The Case of the Exploding Man.

Brian wondered why the cops didn't see that cut on Johnson's hand. He also wondered why the cut on his knee wouldn't scab over.

THE QUEEN IS NOT A GARDEN

ROBERT CAMPBELL

she picks her teeth with a hawthorn barb   grinds bone-meal
for rhizomes   bitch-dander clouds the air   in the empire
flowers are the work of hands   the Queen eats maggots and
ditch-muck   counts finger-bones protruding   from the
graves of botanists   one: *in life   I kept receipts on a bulletin
board*   mold-bloom embellishing a tire   a kudzu-riddled fire
truck   two: *my father's leather ledger*   when the empire was
born the Queen   blessed it with rot and riot   tossed her
infants in its churn   three: *my predictive cloud-based hands
my opioid heart*   today the empire's weatherman   predicts
snow   the Queen is collecting press-on nails   for her newest
iteration of briar   gathers crude and grime for a hex   a dead
horse by the roadside   conjuring flies

TO FIND THE QUEEN YOU MUST KILL ANIMAL-YOU

ROBERT CAMPBELL

by a cold hand   by a silver spool of thread   stretched over
miles of caves   was there a door   a garden gate   how did
we escape the empire   hour of poison   when amanita spores
travel on a song   we came here to find a secret name   hidden
from the empire   the Queen became dark light   and
white-haired root   tunnelling black air   eating worms   the
Queen is phosphorescing in the nucleus   hour of fester and
fern   by starlight   the Queen picks burrs from her monsoon
of jet-black hair   by deadnettle flowers   beside the pond   a
trail of glowing fungi lit the path   beneath the water   we
pulled the password   from a wound   killing animal-me and
animal-you   digging graves for acorns   hour of radishes
blisterwort   skullcap   vigil of limestone   the Queen is
sharpening   her bones   thinking of the empire   sipping
venom

Destroying Angels Are the Queen's Pale Children

ROBERT CAMPBELL

devoid of angle   bulbous and taut, they squat   beneath your
uncle's   sloped pecan tree   cajoling with lichen   in the
worm moon's month   what did you know   about poison
poison   is just like us   if poison   had a face it would be
your face if poison had a name   it would be yours   the
Queen has never killed a soul   once it rained aeroplankton
spores for weeks   no one could see for all   the fungal swarm
this is speaking tumors into flesh   we name mushrooms after
their proprietary horrors   the Queen's white ledger   build
your house on the edge of a ravine   ride a horse into the
sea   these are other fool crimes you know   isn't poison just
another word   for anti-human   unfit   her averse properties
plucking fruit from her white hand   animal-you felt pretty

SILENT SUPPER

ROBERT CAMPBELL

It isn't called this. *Deaf and dumb supper* is what the old folks said, but you wince at the proverbial use of *deaf* and *dumb*. The old folks said *haint* and *spectre*. You lick your lips and mull. *In the foothills of the Appalachian mountains...* No. This isn't the way to begin. Once, a daughter fell hillside, twisted her ankle on a briar. The wagon trail to Ravenna, long-abandoned, is still rumored to be drunk with ghosts: travelers robbed and buried in the sink holes, hidden by tall grass. At night, their heads flicker like a flame above a wick. Kudzu. Deer ticks. You wonder what to tell the reader. How the cows fled down the valley trail? How sad and sorry lonesome places are? That old hitch? *The places we leave keep a certain hunger.* Is this what you mean to say? Once, we knew how to call the dead home. We knew better than to make them knock.

To the Current Tenant

SAMANTHA STEINER

 o the Current Tenant,

I have a relationship with your apartment.

When I was fifteen hours old, my parents brought me to the playground next to your building. My brother zipped around the jungle gym while my dad kept pace from ground level. My mom settled into a bench beneath a tree and held me. We spent a lot of weekends that way, and soon enough, my mom and I were in the sandbox making castles and cakes.

Your living room was another kind of playground for me. I amused myself quietly on the floor while my mom read her magazine. She was still reading when I slipped a hand under the carpet, fished out whatever gunk had accumulated there, and stowed it in my mouth. She turned the page and looked up.

"No, Samantha! No, no!"

In a sort of reversal of a mother bird depositing food into her baby's beak, my mom probed my mouth with two fingers and extracted the soggy mess.

When I learned to handle a crayon, little marks began appearing on the hallway moldings. A yellow dot, a green line. They looked as though they had landed there by accident. No one noticed. The marks climbed to the doorknobs. Then as high as I could reach. 2AM appeared on the wall in number two pencil. My first grade teacher told my dad I had developed outstanding handwriting.

Finally, my dad spotted a waxy blue backslash over the couch.

"Sam," he said, kneeling to make eye contact.

I studied my shoes. Whenever my dad tried to be stern, he sounded like the dads on TV. Have you finished your homework? Go to your room. These lines, coming from the man who usually laughed when I called him dude. His tone was almost as patronizing as my attitude toward him: every so often, I figured, he needed to be reassured that he was in charge.

"Come on," he said. "You know better."

I resisted smiling until he walked away. A few days later, there was a fresh sprinkle of unseen graffiti in my parents' bedroom.

My own room had more conventional decoration. I plastered the wall over my bed with stickers from an aquarium gift shop. There were seashells in cream and pale purple, swaying foliage and mounds of glitter-flecked sand. At bedtime, when the room was washed in syrupy light from the street below, the seascape turned a phosphorescent green. It was as enchanting as it was ominous.

Laughter and echoing footsteps leaked in through the closed window. Perhaps my imagination had been primed by too many episodes of *Scooby-Doo*. On the other side of the window, I pictured, was a cobblestone street lined with gaslights. A mob was brandishing pitchforks and lighting torches, preparing to burn the city down. My attempts to gaslight my parents had been laughably bad, but the gaslights I conjured in my own mind illuminated a view right into hell.

My brother and I crawled under blankets. My dad sat by my brother's bed while my mom sat by mine. After a few minutes, they switched places.

"Hug," I commanded each parent on their turn with me. "Hug. Hug. Hug."

In my mind, fire ravaged the streets. I continued my metronomic request until the parent at my side leaned down. Through the blankets, I felt a set of arms around my shoulders like angel wings.

Those nights ended just before my tenth birthday. It was in the living room, the scene of so many birthday parties, playdates, visits from relatives, that our parents told us we would be moving. I was sitting on the couch. My feet were on the same carpet whose fluff I had once tried to ingest. I could have leaned over and touched the waxy blue backslash that hadn't faded.

I stood in the living room while unsmiling men lifted furniture onto dollies. There was an island of boxes where the couch had been. The place looked so strange, with wide stretches and then clusters of detail, the jutted lip around the doorway, the accordion fold of the closet doors, the sudden way the hallway opened up into the living room, the light fixtures and white cords stapled along the molding. Bare planes, walls and ceiling, stretched on and on and then met at a corner and disappeared into each other. I was looking at the inside of the strongbox that been home to my most creative and destructive urges.

At eye level, the beige paint bumped and dipped in a way that made it seem like it was still wet, but over the doorways, in the places we had never stained with the oil of our hair and skin, it was light and chalky. On the ceiling, freckles of shadow clustered around the light fixtures and windows. I emblazoned the inside of my skull with the image of the apartment's skeleton, to gather the scraps that would have to sustain me for a lifetime of remembering.

I watched one of the men hold up an open-faced box of books while another passed a roll of packing tape over the top. Directly onto a book jacket with a cartoon of a child on a candy-colored mountain. Oh, the Places You'll Go. In a few days, I would sit on the floor of a different living room and peel the tape slowly, taking the paper with it, and then the child's body would be suspended over not a mountain, but a chasm.

Your apartment probably looks different now. Maybe someone else has found a canvas in those walls. But I'm still burning to revisit the temple of my earliest memories. It would be a way of drawing the past into the present. I was hoping I could stop by sometime.

Sincerely,
Samantha Steiner

short story

THE WITCH FATHER

HEATHER RICK

The University of West Virginia holds a curious object in its collection. Many experts do not like to acknowledge that it exists; it would not do well for the public to know, they say. In the basement of the archives you can find it, if you know the right people and are persuasive and discrete. At the end of a long row of metal shelves, an attendant will remove a box bearing a label that reads: "Discovered in the vicinity of the Monongahela National Forest in 1911. Materials - human skin, feathers, silver. Anthropologists believe this to be a fetish object for a cult, perhaps used in the practice of witchcraft. Local tribes denies any indigenous origin to the object. Tentatively attributed to early 18th century Scotch-Irish settlers."

More than this, no one at the University can tell. Only a handful of researchers have taken a professional interest in the object, and the University has never encouraged their endeavors. Those who have handled the object report that there is something unwholesome about it. Even those researchers who approach it with the most interest and zeal end by being thankful that the University is wise enough not to display it; some have expressed the wish that the University would simply incinerate the object.

History, however, is not merely that which is recorded in textbooks and acknowledged by universities. True history is etched into the land itself and broods in the memory of mountain and tree. And if a lust for true history brings you to the basement of the archives, you would be better off taking your curiosities to the Monongahela itself, at the rambling foothills of the Alleghenies. And again, if you were persuasive and discrete, this is the true story which nature might yield, borne to your ears on the wings of robins and crows.

The baby had a glass eye and it kept falling out.

Each time, the mother would pick it up, blow the dust from it, roll it between her palms, and pop it back in. The baby showed no interest in this routine, merely continuing its business of drooling and pawing at its mother's dress and shawl with the calm indifference of an ascetic. The baby's face did not appear to be injured or disfigured. When it looked up from the designs of sticky spit it had painted, one merely saw the crystal glitter of a blue glass eye. Even when the eye fell out, and the soft white flower petal of the eyelid wilted in on itself, one saw no raw red socket, nor the pucker of scarred flesh. It was merely as though the baby had left one eye in the womb, abandoned there to observe forever the inner cosmos - the scarlet placental sea, the moist sky of tessellated tissue, constellations of blood vessels - while the other eye was content with the small gray universe of the one-room cabin where the baby spent its days, crawling on the stone floor by the hearth or cocooned in its cradle while the mother cooked and cleaned.

When the baby was born, a curiously quiet and bloodless birth, the midwife was the first to notice the deformity. She was a dark-eyed old woman and the things she carried were many and mossy with memories of the old country. The talismans in her apron were dusty with old meanings that a people Christianized and removed to a new land, clung to without remembering why. She carried them still, for it was the midwife's duty to guard against the unseen and unexpected, and new beginnings of all kinds were her territory. As the mother had slept in her bed of sweat and the baby wriggled silently in its wrappings, the father and midwife had exchanged sorrowful looks. Before leaving, she'd whispered to him that this was a bad sign, that there was no good in store for such a child - it was best disposed of before it became a sorrow to all. But at that moment, the mother awoke and demanded her baby. The midwife shook her head, pulled the glass eye from the pocket of her apron, breathed what benedictions she knew onto it, and pressed it into the father's palm.

The glass eye was more alive than the real one. The eye of gelatinous tissue and delicate vessels revealed only an idiot baby-consciousness, groping clumsily through its small dusty world for food and attention, while the eye of tessellated aquamarine glass glimmered with an awareness and intelligence unsettling to observe in an infant. It followed the father about the room and glinted in the dark when the starlight rapped its brittle knuckles against the windowpanes.

Sometimes when the eye fell out the baby's hands would scuttle across the floor, like some bloated spider that had crawled up from a sunless world, to snatch up the orb and put it in the wet greedy mouth. The fat lips puckered and make gibbering, sucking noises around the eye until the mother forced them open and returned the eye to the socket, shining with spittle.

One day the eye vanished. The mother thought the baby had finally swallowed it. Glass eyes were hard to come by, and the father insisted they could not beg the midwife for another, as likely that had been her only one. For a while they tried different things in place of the missing eye. They tried a smooth, round river rock, but it was too heavy and the baby's head always listed to the right. There was a ripe scarlet cherry, but it gave the mother a fright one morning when she discovered it had burst in the night, covering the sleeping baby's face in purple-red flesh and tiny maggots. The mother even tried the bell from the cat's collar, but the father swore the noise drove him to distraction and the cat was jealous. The baby was not happy with any of the substitutes and would cry until its bloated face appeared ready to burst. Finally the mother took to covering the baby's face with the yellow veil, and this seemed to calm it. Behind its mask of semi-transparent cloth the baby clucked and cooed to itself in the corner of the kitchen, the fanciful firelight on its chubby body casting a shadow on the whitewashed wall like a deformed troll king on its subterranean throne.

It was spring and the mother had washing to do. She set the baby in the grass beneath a gnarled rowan to amuse itself with bits of bugs and new flowers while she hung the quilts and dresses. A bird's nest had fallen from the tree and the chubby groping fingers chanced upon the smooth domes of the little eggs, warmed by the sunlight. The clumsy tumult of the baby's laughter whipped through the wind-tossed sheets on the line. Going over to the rowan, the mother saw the baby's veil, crushed egg-yolk yellow, on the emerald grass. In the socket was one of the eggs – a robin's, the same brilliant blue of the real eye. The baby laughed and flapped its doughy arms with pride and satisfaction. The egg was an improvement over the barren socket and it didn't fall out like the glass eye used to, so the mother let the baby keep it.

Spring waxed green in the world outside. From its cradle by the lead-paned window the baby could watch the eastern constellations dance their slow waltz. The mother noticed how wakeful yet quiet the baby was on these nights, as though the new eye offered it visions of nature's mysteries, almost as if the eye could read the hieroglyphics of the stars. The father watched the mother watching the baby watching the stars, and the nights were long for him.

There came a week of rain when the baby was confined to its corner in the kitchen, between the hearth and the storm-beaten window. The fire sputtered low and the streaming rain and warped glass turned the world outside into a phantasmagoric blur of grey sky and green leaves. The mother had soaked bits of bread in a bowl of milk for the baby. It sat on the floor, gumming the soggy bread and splashing bluish-white milk onto the stone-flagged floor. There was a sudden squeal of surprise and flakes of brilliant blue shell freckled the bowl of milk. Into the sulphurous gloom of the kitchen piped a song like wind-tossed leaves. Out of the fragments of shell that stuck in the socket, a baby robin peeped, its feathers new-grey and soft. The baby lifted a soaking hunk of bread to its face and laughed as the bird began to eat.

Before long they were forced to banish the cat to the barn. It had taken to perching on the windowsill above the cradle, all rigid muscle and unblinking gaze. As soon as the robin chirped or rustled in its fleshy nest, the cat would stalk the baby, its sinuous black shape pacing a tightening circle around the cradle. The baby was fond of its guest and began to cry whenever the cat drew near, tossing its wooden toys at the prowling feline. The father was no more pleased than the cat, but he kept his silence and his distance.

Summer broadened in the sky and bronzed the apples on the trees and the corn in the fields. The robin had grown into its colors - an orange breast and grey-brown body. It was now so large that it had to squeeze and wriggle its way into the baby's eye socket when it returned at sundown from a day of hunting grubs. Bird feces ran down the baby's cheeks and cracked and dried on its clothes. It was always puffing feathers out of its chubby wet lips and putting them in its wisps of golden hair, try as the mother would to keep it clean. The baby was only quiet and calm when the robin was nested in its eye socket, the black eyes and yellow beak peeping from beneath the gold-lashed lid. Only then did it stop its fidgeting and squawking and sit, content. In the evenings the mother tried to sponge off some of the feces while the baby and the bird cooed to each other, and the father and the cat sat on the opposite side of the room together, coolly indifferent, yet watching.

Winter was building in the dense wooly clouds on the horizon, twining itself about the bare branches of the gnarled rowan in the yard. The wild birds took to the sky in great flocks and speckled the reaped fields with the chiaroscuro of their flight. The robin was restless and the baby was quiet. With all the bustle of preparing for winter, the reaping and slaughtering, preserving and canning, the mother had no time to combat the baby's mess. It sat in its corner by the hearth, a little monster of filth, covered in feces and feathers and the bits of twigs and leaves the robin had collected for its nest. It was quieter than ever, as if it too sensed the approach of winter and the urge to migrate beyond the little gray world of the kitchen and yard. The father stroked the cat and brooded, unable to bear the thought of a whole winter spent confined to the one-room cabin with the creature that was his child and the guest that had become so much a part of it, until the one almost had no identity without the other.

On the last day of autumn, the father went to see the midwife. She'd chosen for her home the ruins of an old stone fort, and had constructed a lean-to against it. A stone wall as tall as the father rode the ridges of the south side of the mountain, the side that looked toward the new settlements. The local tribes said that one could see such fortifications on scattered mountains, that the mossy stones had kept watch since before any man, white or red, had walked the land. The Indians did not build near such ruins, fearing the orbs of light they claimed traversed the length of the fortifications. The new settlers, the images of fairy rings and standing stones and giants' causeways still fresh in their memories, followed their example. But the midwife felt a great power from those old stones and she did not fear the old things. She chose for her lean-to a spot where the wall rose into a single finger of stone, a narrow tower with no door that reached toward the kaleidoscope of leaves in the summer and brooded on the patterns of stars in the winter.

When the father arrived at the door of her lean-to, snow on his hat and fear in his eyes, she knew why he'd come. She brewed them strong tea in little stone mugs and told him what she suspected. She told him stories of the little people, of mothers who awoke on fine mornings to discover their healthy pink babies replaced by the greenish-grey shriveled cubs of the little people. The hidden race sometimes stole human babies for their rituals and sacrifices, leaving their own to be raised by unwitting human parents. Sometimes they even impregnated a woman who found herself wandering alone across the moors after dark on nights of the full moon. Could this be the case with the father's wife? There had been many days during the first settling of the land when he was clearing trees and brush, tilling the virgin soil, hauling stones from the old hilltop forts, aiding with the construction of cabins, when she'd been left alone in this wild new land. The little people, who were to be found anywhere wilderness still brooded, never suffered encroachment passively.

She gave the father instructions for the purging of the fairy child. He shuddered at the details but hardened his resolve at the memory of the robin squeezing its feathery bulk into the eye socket of the giggling baby. Returning home, he did not go to bed but rather to the barn, where he began to make a small noose out of a length of rope.

On the first full moon of winter, when the moon-shadows capered silver-blue across the acres of snow, the father brewed a strong tea of pungent roots the midwife had given him. A cup of it put the mother to sleep, and he began his work. He knotted one end of the noose around a branch of the rowan in the yard and passed the loop around the baby's neck. The little body cast fantastic shadows on the snow as it writhed like a fat white grub at the end of a fishhook, yet it was silent but for a

> The little body cast fantastic shadows on the snow as it writhed like a fat white grub at the end of a fishhook.

gurgle at the end that might have been a laugh. The father crushed the robin in his fist and threw it to the cat. Following the midwife's instructions, he let the baby hang for the rest of the night so the moonlight could cure the corpse. As he lay beneath the scratchy quilt, his back to the frost-rimed windows, he could see the moon-gilded silhouette of the hanging baby on the stone floor. He turned his face to the wall and descended into abyssal dreams of tree roots and earthen walls and laughter in the dark.

In the morning he cut into the frozen body with his big slaughtering knife, scraped out the entrails, and buried them beneath the rowan tree. Crows watched his work from the branches and volleyed their calls across the frozen fields. He cleaned and stretched the skin over a fire banked with cedar and the bundles of dried herbs the midwife had given him. The mother awoke late and groggy, disturbed by the silence and the look the cat gave her as it sprawled in front of the fire licking its whiskers and claws. When the father came in, his hands ruddy and blackened from his work, she looked at his face and asked no questions. It was as though the eye that had remained inside of her had given her a second sight, a ghost vision, and somehow she'd known such a thing would come to pass. She neglected her work, the spinning and canning, and when a warm week came and the snows receded a bit, she packed her belongings in a basket and returned across the county to her own people. She told them nothing definite, but the hints she let slip during ever more frequent bouts of drinking disturbed her family and neighbors. Some talked of paying the farm a visit, but those older and wiser, with deeper memories of the old country, counseled patience.

The father continued the task the midwife had set him. When the skin had smoked and dried, he sewed it back together with hog sinew and a bone needle. He stuffed it with things displeasing to the little people – bits of iron, sweet herbs, root of mandrake and crows' feathers. He gave it hair of dried sweetgrass and plugged lumps of iron under the puckered eyelids, weaved the midnight green feathers into a chain about its neck. There it sat, finally, by the hearth as it had in life, a little shriveled mummy doll of the creature that had been his son. With the doll acting as a kind of talisman, the spell of the little people would be broken this way, the midwife explained, and never would they be able to trouble his family or his property again. The cat curled up on the chair beside it and napped. As the embers burned low on the dark nights, the father saw the dull iron eyes of the doll eat up the last spark of light and welcome a gloom as of inner earth.

It was not the dark nights that troubled the father though, so much as the moonlit ones. When he awoke on nights when the moon sailed high and full, he would again see the black outline of the hanging baby cat on the stone floor, wriggling in the bone-bleached light. But always when he sprang from bed to the windowsill, there was nothing hanging from the rowan branches. Always an icy, sleepless spell awaited him when he returned to his already-cold bed, as the doll watched the dull iron hours of the night pass over him from its seat by the hearth.

Now the loneliness and isolation of winter are something to blame, as is a guilty conscience, but it is also the truth that a man who has once stepped a foot over the boundary into another world does not easily step back, not without the mysterious black mud of fairyland clinging to his boots and pants. Winter melted into a spring of clammy rains and rotting vegetation. The work of the farm was neglected; the fields were not planted that year and the animals began to go feral. The land, so lately and lightly wrested from the forest and brought under man's dominion, fell wild again and nature began the work of reclamation. The ashes were not swept from the hearth, as the mother once had done, but crept into the corners of the cabin, into the cat's whiskers and the father's unkempt beard. He woke up scratching his face in the night to discover tiny bits of blue eggshell in the tangled roots of his beard. Still he did not shave it.

On a midwinter day, when the shadows of crows were frozen on the fields of crusted snow and a bitter mist crept down from the mountain to melt the hard clear corners of the sunlit world, the father set out to see the midwife. He'd left a fire of smoking rowan branches burning on the hearth and did not close the door behind him. The cat followed him down the slush-churned path that led from the cabin to the woods. The air was wooly and clammy with an approaching fog and the only color in the woods was the sharp poisonous red of the winterberries which grew in thickets as one approached the midwife's dwelling.

The father's feet dragged heavy in the snow in their leather-bound rags, his body sluggish with the weight of toxic dreams that came on sleepless nights, when his eyes lay open to the white goblin-moon. He carried the doll in a sack, wrapped in dried cornhusks fastened with iron nails. It seemed much heavier than it once was, as though it gained weight, brooded, grew as the baby never would. The mist darkened as he approached the cabin and it caught long dry fingers at his throat. It was only when the charred timbers and smoking logs emerged did he realize it was smoke. The cabin had been burned, the stone tower daubed with signs of banishment with charcoal from the fire. He could not understand why the midwife, whose ministrations had been tolerated for so long by a people superstitious and desirous of aid in a new land, could have suddenly met such a violent end. It was then for the first time in months that he remembered his wife, the dull look of knowing she had worn in the days after the purging, and knew that she must have talked enough for the villagers to make their own deductions.

So he was alone now. The cat slipped between the father's legs and leapt atop one of the tallest stones, surveying the smoking ruins with cold yellow eyes. The father sunk against the base of the tower. He was alone with the silence of winter and death, and with the doll. Even the cat was still, curled atop the wall, and no birds called in the mist. Embers glowed in the remains of the fire, and among them the father saw long bones black with charred flesh and the white half moon of a shattered skull, the last clumps of hair burning with a dank stench that choked him. With a portion of the skull he scooped the glowing embers into a pile at the base of the tower, blowing on them and stoking them with the sweet-smelling cleansing grasses that were woven into his beard. The fire rose and licked the base of the tower and he fed it with the remaining wood from the lean-to. He would burn the doll, release the spirit of the changeling back to the little people of the hills. Maybe then he would leave these hills and his farm, make for one of the cities on the coast where he could grow old away from forests and mountains, stones and birds, and forget that he'd ever been a father.

The flames grew brighter as the early winter night crept down from the eaves of the mountain to roost in the crevices of the wall. The fire crackled and the subtle things of the night began to chipper and moan and peep, the misty winter woods coming to sightless life beyond the enchanted circle of firelight. When the fire was strong, he removed the doll from his sack. It felt heavier yet again, and as he unfastened the iron nails he thought he detected movement through the cornhusks. The cat on its perch began to hiss and pounce, swiping at something unseen in the dark air that swooped and dove at it.

The father spread the cornhusks and the plump pink form of the baby wriggled in its papery cocoon, giggling at the play of firelight on its father's wild beard.

A burning like rancid gorge rose in his throat as he looked into the creature's face. In the socket which had held the glass eye and housed the robin there was a living eye, perhaps the eye it had left in the womb. Silver and round as the moon, it bulged from the socket, twice as large as the other eye. It did not blink. A cold silver light closed over the father, eclipsing the red glow of the fire. On the wall above he heard the cat let out a screech that descended into a gurgling whimper, then a sound as of wings and chirping, like a tree full of birds on a spring morning. From inside the tower came three knocks and the baby giggled in gleeful greeting.

Small squat shapes emerged over the lip of the wall, fat white bodies, plump as worms that feed on the rot and refuse of inner earth, and in their faces were silver eyes. Perhaps they were the architects of the old fortifications, and perhaps they were the true fathers of the baby, and then again perhaps they were merely the shapes of the father's madness, specters of moonlight and smoke. Whatever their provenance, their ragged circle pulled tighter around the cowering man The father shut his eyes as the baby's fingers squirmed into his beard.

In the clear light of a day without mist or snow, the villagers returned to the mountain. A few hunters, straying near to the old fortifications in pursuit of their quarry, had reported sounds from where the midwife's lean-to had recently stood. Reluctantly, the whispered words and fears of the mother still echoing despite the cleansing they had performed, the old men of the village once again set out for the old fortifications. At the foot of the tower, where a fire more recent than theirs still smoked, they found a shrunken figure. Skin cured like leather, hair and beard stiff and dry as grass. Feathers and bird feces caked the face. Under the puckered eyelids were lumps of silver, reflecting a moon that was not visible in the sky above. A glass eye was in its mouth. They buried it at the foot of the tower and never went to the mountain again.

> **Under the puckered eyelids were lumps of silver, reflecting a moon that was not visible in the sky above.**

Decades passed, a century. The country lost something of its wildness. Cities grew like mushrooms where the early settlers had planted their villages. With the turn of another century the government began to preserve forests from the booming population, and the mountain with its mysterious fortifications was set aside for wildlife and archeological research. The object was discovered in the tower and was sent to the state university where it remains to this day, in a metal drawer in the archives bearing a placard with the bare antiseptic details and foggy attribution. It is as though the scientists and the anthropologists have intuited from it something of the old villagers' fear, and that they too wish to forget, without knowing why, without knowing anything definite.

The excavators knew more. They could perhaps have told you of the unusual profusion of robins on that mountaintop, even in autumn, and how they could not keep any workers from the nearby reservation. And maybe some, who were descended from the Scotch-Irish settlers, would have told you of the nameless unease they felt at the site, like the prickling of old memories. And maybe the lead archeologist, who drank too much and was prone to unprofessional flights of fancy that many blamed on his study of Indian folklore, could have told you how, working late on a night of the full moon, he heard the giggle of a baby from deep within the ground beneath the tower, and asked to be taken off the project the next day.

And the stones and trees could tell you even more, but men have lost touch with them, and perhaps that is not to be mourned. The land folds her secrets and her strange children to her bosom. ❦

CONTRIBUTOR NOTES

Samia Ahmed is an MFA Creative Writing student at Old Dominion University. She is originally from India where she has been published in nationally recognized journals. She has a master's in journalism. She believes in breaking stereotypes and continues to practice it while petting pretty black cats and sipping chai.

Craig Anderson is a writer, trainer and part-time palm reader who lives in St. Petersburg, Florida (but will always consider himself a Detroiter). His work has appeared in *Glitterwolf Magazine, the Eckerd Review, Former Cactus*, and other publications. You can find him on twitter at @wildcraigdom.

Andy Betz has tutored and taught in excess of 30 years. His novel, short stories, and poems are works still defining his style. He lives in 1974, has been married for 27 years, and collects occupations (the current tally is 100). His works are found everywhere a search engine operates.

Katharina Bezushko is a single parent who has spent several years pouring her love of language into the ears of her children, and is now endeavoring to share her words with a new audience.

J V Birch lives in Adelaide. Her poems have been published in anthologies, journals and magazines across Australia, the UK, Canada and the US. She has three chapbooks and a full-length collection with Ginninderra Press, and blogs at www.jvbirch.com.

Just Buffalo Literary Center teaching artist **Benjamin Brindise** is the author of the chapbook ROTTEN KID (Ghost City Press, 2017), the full length collection of poetry *Those Who Favor Fire, Those Who Pray to Fire* (EMP Books, 2018), and the short fiction micro chap *The Procession* (Ghost City Press, 2018). He has represented Buffalo, NY in the National Poetry Slam in 2015, 2016, and 2018, helping Buffalo to place as high as 9th in the country. His poetry and fiction has been published widely online and in print including *Maudlin House, Trailer Park Quarterly,* and *Philosophical Idiot*.

Robert Campbell is the author of the chapbook In the Herald of Improbable Misfortunes (Etchings Press, 2018). His poems have appeared in Tupelo Quarterly, Columbia Poetry Review, Ninth Letter, and many other journals. He holds an M.F.A. in Creative Writing from Murray State University and an M.S. in Library Science from the University of Kentucky. Read more about him at robertjcampbell.wordpress.com.

CONTRIBUTOR NOTES

Dan A. Cardoza has an MS Degree in Education from UC, Sacramento, Calif. He is the author of four poetry Chapbooks, and a new book of fiction, *Second Stories*. His work has appeared in *101 Words, Adelaide, Australia, California Quarterly, Chaleur, Cleaver, Confluence, UK, Dissections, Door=Jar, Drabble, Entropy, Esthetic Apostle, Foxglove, Frogmore, UK, High Shelf Press, Poetry Northwest, Rue Scribe, Runcible Spoon, Skylight 47, Spelk, Spillwords, Fiction Pool, Stray Branch, Urban Arts, Zen Space, Tulpa, Australia* and *Zeroflash*.

Marisa Crane is a lesbian fiction writer and poet. Her work has appeared or is forthcoming in *Jellyfish Review, Pithead Chapel, Maudlin House, Cotton Xenomorph, Okay Donkey, Occulum*, and elsewhere.

Evelyn Deshane's creative and nonfiction work has appeared in The Atlantic's tech channel, *Plenitude Magazine, Briarpatch Magazine, Strange Horizons, Lackington's*, and *Bitch Magazine*, among other publications. Evelyn (pron. Eve-a-lyn) received an MA from Trent University's Public Texts Program and is currently completing a PhD at the University of Waterloo. Their most recent project, #Trans, is an anthology about transgender and nonbinary identity online. For more information, check out evedeshane.wordpress.com.

Sean William Dever is a Boston-based poet, educator, and activist currently in his last year of his MFA in Creative Writing with a focus in Poetry at Emerson College. He teaches writing at Emerson and Boston Architectural College. In addition, he also works as a Professional ESL Tutor at Northeastern University. He is the author of the chapbook, *I've Been Cancelling Appointments with My Psychiatrist for Two Years Now*, May 2019, published by Swimming with Elephants Publications.

S. Preston Duncan is a writer, caregiver, and BBQist in Richmond, Virginia, and is currently training as an End of Life Doula. A spiritual mutt (read: half Jewish, half Americana music), he is a denominational Antifascist Southern River Rat and devout pilgrim of coastal climes. Recent aspirations include becoming the Jason Isbell of literature, stealing death's laughter, and transcendental pimento cheese. He is the former Senior Editor of local arts and culture publication, RVA Magazine. His work has appeared in *Bottom Shelf Whiskey* and *RVA Magazine* (no, not while he was editor).

RC deWinter's poetry is anthologized in *New York City Haiku* (NY Times, 2017), *Uno: A Poetry Anthology* (Verian Thomas, 2002), *Cowboys & Cocktails: Poetry from the True Grit Saloon* (Brick Street Poetry, April 2019) in print in *2River View, Meat For Tea: The Valley Review, Pink Panther Magazine, Down in the Dirt, Scarlet Leaf Review, Genre Urban Arts* and in numerous online literary journals.

CONTRIBUTOR NOTES

Linda Dove holds a Ph.D. in Renaissance literature and teaches college writing. She is also an award-winning poet, and her books include, *In Defense of Objects* (2009), *O Dear Deer*, (2011), *This Too* (2017), and the scholarly collection of essays, *Women, Writing, and the Reproduction of Culture in Tudor and Stuart Britain* (2000). Poems have been nominated for a Pushcart Prize and the Robert H. Winner Award from the Poetry Society of America. She lives with her human family, two Jack Russell terriers, and three backyard chickens in the foothills east of Los Angeles, where she serves as the faculty editor of *MORIA Literary Magazine* at Woodbury University.

Meiloni Erickson is a California native who enjoys living in different parts of the country including Alaska, Louisiana, and currently Pennsylvania. She holds an MFA from the University of New Orleans, where she served as Fiction Editor for *Bayou Magazine*. Her fiction has been published in *The Greenbriar Review*, *Flyway Journal*, and *Natural Bridge*.

Ken Farrell's work is forthcoming/published in journals such as *Sport Literate*, *The Piltdown Review*, *The Offbeat* (poetry prize winner, selected be Heid E. Erdrich), *Pilgrimage*, *The Texas Poetry Journal*, *Writer's Bloc*, *Connections*, and anthologized with *Arachne Press*. He holds an MFA from Texas State University and an MA from Salisbury University, has earned bread as an adjunct, server, professional cage fighter, and pizzaiolo, and for most of the past ten years, he's worked in a warehouse. He is currently busy with family and revising and shopping poetry and short fiction manuscripts, and in response to a challenge from his daughter who participated in NaNoWriMo, he recently began his first novel.

Ginny Fite's stories have appeared in *Fluent Magazine*, the *Delmarva Review*, and *Temenos*. A collection of linked short stories, titled Stronger in Heaven, was long-listed for the 2017 Santa Fe Writers Project contest. Ginny is the author of the mysteries *Cromwell's Folly*, *No Good Deed Left Undone*, and *Lying, Cheating & Occasionally Murder*, and the political thriller *No End of Bad*. Her degrees are from Rutgers University and Johns Hopkins University and she has studied at the School for Women Healers and the Maryland Poetry Therapy Institute.

Catherine Garbinsky is a writer, a witch, and a worrier living in Northern California. She holds a degree in The Poetics of Transformation: Creative Writing, Religion, and Social Justice from the University of Redlands. Catherine's chapbook of Ursula Le Guin erasures, *All Spells Are Strong Here*, is part of the Ghost City Press 2018 Summer Series. Her work has been featured or is forthcoming in *L'éphémére Review*, *Rose Quartz Journal*, *Venefica Magazine*, *Cauldron Anthology*, and others.

CONTRIBUTOR NOTES

Gerri R. Gray adores the absurd and the abnormal; therefore, that's what she writes about. That's what she needs to write about. Her debut novel, *The Amnesia Girl*, was published by HellBound Books in 2017. Her second and third books, *Gray Skies of Dismal Dreams* and *The Graveyard Girls*, respectively, were published in 2018. Her poetry and prose have appeared in numerous literary journals and anthologies, including *Beautiful Tragedies*; *Demons, Devils & Denizens of Hell 2*; *EconoClash*; *Deadman's Tome Cthulhu Christmas Special: Other Lovecraftian Yuletide Tales*; and *Mixed Bag of Horror*.

Tim Hanson lives in Santa Monica, CA, and works as a substitute school teacher. His short story 'Broken Bottles' appeared in great weather for MEDIA's 2014 anthology I Let Go of the Stars in My Hand.

A young writer from Yorkshire, **Emily Harrison** has recently discovered that she actually likes creative writing, despite everything she may have previously said. She can be found on Twitter @emily__harrison, and has had work published with *Storgy, Soft Cartel, Retreat West* and *Riggwelter Press,* to name a few.

Rachel Hehl (yes, that's her real surname) is a twenty-four-year-old demonic entity from Melbourne, Australia. She likes iced coffee, Byronic heroes, and all things sparkly.

Courtney Hilden's work has been published in Bustle, More of Us, Panning for Poems, Dodging the Rain, among others.

Wendy Howe is an English teacher and freelance writer who lives in Southern California. Her poetry reflects her interest in myth, diverse landscapes and ancient cultures. Over the years, she has been published in an assortment of journals both on-line and in print. Among them: *The Linnet's Wings, Ariadne's Thread, Mirror Dance, Strange Horizons, Niteblade, Goblin Fruit, Mythic Delirium, Scheherezade's Bequest,* and *Yellow Medicine Review*. Some of her latest work will be forthcoming in *The Peacock Journal* and *Poetry Pacific*.

Recently retired, **Julie Allyn Johnson** enjoys photography, baking bread, hiking, biking, traveling with her husband, crochet, playing with her new puppy and reading about writing and poetry. Last summer, when inspiration started to keep her awake at night, poetry ensued. She is the oldest of six girls and grew up surrounded by oak, walnut and other woods native to north central Iowa piled high around the ten-acre backyard out back behind her father's sawmill. Julie has been writing poetry for a year and a half. She has been published in *Lyrical Iowa, Persephone's Daughters* and *Typishly*. Her writing process is varied. She has journals stashed throughout the house and in the car and always carries a small notebook in her purse. Sometimes she goes weeks and weeks without so much as a journal entry and other times, writes several times a day.

Contributor Notes

Alex Kazemi lives in Auckland, New Zealand where he works as a doctor and moves in and out of some strange worlds. He is an emerging writer and has had work accepted for publication in *Thin Air Magazine*. Generally speaking, he doesn't mind the dark.

Cecilia Kennedy earned a PhD in Spanish literature from Ohio State University. Her speculative fiction works have appeared in *Theme of Absence, Gathering Storm Literary Magazine, Down in the Dirt Literary Magazine,* and *The Sirens Call Ezine*. She lives in the Greater Seattle area with her family and details her "scary" attempts at DIY projects in her blog, "Fixin' Leaks and Leeks." https://fixinleaksnleeksdiy.blog/.

Gregory Kimbrell is the author of *The Primitive Observatory* (Southern Illinois University Press, 2016), winner of the 2014 Crab Orchard Series in Poetry First Book Award, and The Ceremonial Armor of the Impostor (Weasel Press, forthcoming). His poems have appeared or are forthcoming in *Abyss & Apex, Fearsome Critters, IDK Magazine, Impossible Archetype, The Operating System, Otoliths,* and elsewhere. More of his writing, including his sci-fi/horror magnetic poems and erasures, can be found at gregorykimbrell.com.

A. C. Koch's work has been published in the *Columbia Journal, Mississippi Review,* and *Exquisite Corpse,* and two of his short stories have been awarded first place in the Raymond Carver Short Story Award (2003, 2007). He lives in Denver where he teaches linguistics at the University of Colorado and plays guitar in a bossa nova trio, Firstimers.

C. Kubasta writes poetry, prose and hybrid forms. She is the author of several poetry books, most recently *OF COVENANTS* (Whitepoint, 2017). Her fiction includes *GIRLING* (Brain Mill, 2017) and *THIS BUSINESS OF THE FLESH* (Apprentice House, 2018). She is active with the Wisconsin Fellowship of Poets, and serves as Assistant Poetry editor with *Brain Mill Press*. Find her at www.ckubasta.com and follow her @CKubastathePoet.

December Lace is a former professional wrestler and pinup model. She has appeared in the *Chicago Tribune,* the *Chicago Sun-Times, Pro Wrestling Illustrated, The Molotov Cocktail, The Cabinet of Heed, Vamp Cat,* and *Rhythm & Bones YANYR Anthology,* among others, as well as the forthcoming *Ghostlight, The Magazine of Terror,* and *Rhythm & Bones Dark Marrow*. She loves Batman, burlesque, cats, and horror movies. She can be found on Twitter @TheMissDecember, http://decemberlace.blogspot.com, or in Chicago's obscure bookshops.

CONTRIBUTOR NOTES

Andrew Lafleche is an award-winning poet and author of six books. His work uses a spoken style of language to blend social criticism, philosophical reflection, explicit language, and black comedy. Andrew enlisted in the Army in 2007 and received an honorable discharge in 2014. Visit www.AJLafleche.com for more information.

Owen Lubozynski is a freelance writer and editor living in the Twin Cities. Copy is her bread and butter; poetry is her jam.

Zuri McWhorter is a Black lady writer from Detroit, MI, USA. Focusing on the things that drive us to be human — patience, humor, redemption, love.

Shanna Merceron is a Florida writer in the second year of her MFA at Hollins University in Roanoke, Virginia. She is at work on a short story collection thesis that explores the dark and strange. When not writing, she is an English language teacher and photographer.

Bekkie Jean Murphy writes in Atlanta, Ga. A Georgia Southern University graduate, she currently works for the Atlanta Ballet, and her work has appeared in *The Coil*.

Victoria Nordlund received her MALS from Wesleyan University. She teaches creative writing at Rockville High School in Vernon, CT. She is also an adjunct professor at the University of Connecticut. A 2018 Best of the Net Nominee, her work is published in *Coffin Bell*, *Pank Magazine*, *Gone Lawn*, *Ghost Proposal*, *Philosophical Idiot*, and other journals. She lives in Connecticut with her husband, three children, and poodle.

Valin Paige is a spoken word poet living in St. Paul, MN. She has a spoken word album titled *Bleed Through* and is published on *Button Poetry*. She is currently an MFA student at Hamline University.

Ralph Pennel is the author of *A World Less Perfect for Dying In*, published by Cervena Barva Press. Ralph's writing has appeared or is forthcoming in *The Iowa Review*, *Literary Orphans*, *F(r)iction*, *Tarpaulin Sky*, *Reality Beach*, *Elm Leaves Journal*, *Rain Taxi Review of Books* and various other publications. His work has been nominated for a Pushcart, and he was twice a finalist for Somerville Poet Laureate. Ralph is on the board of the New England Poetry Club and teaches poetry and writing at Bentley University.

Contributor Notes

Dean Quarrell was born in 1946, in Springfield, Massachusetts. He has so far survived public schools, community college, and university (his baccalaureate degree is in English but written in Latin), the US Air Force, various employment, and retirement. His work has been published in *Dark Ink Magazine* and scheduled for publication in *Chicago Literati*'s Daily Flash. He lives and writes in New Hampshire.

Linda Quinlan has been published in many journals, some of which include *The North Carolina Literary Review, Fine Madness, Pudding, The New Orleans Review* and *Sinister Wisdom*. Linda was Poet of the Year in Wisconsin, and presently lives in Vermont.

James Raleigh is a twenty-one-year-old writer from Brooklyn, New York. He recently graduated from Stevens Institute of Technology with a bachelor's degree in Biomedical Engineering and a minor in Pre-Law and Policy. "Joey: The Magical Axolotl" is his first published piece.

Heather Rick is a native of Worcester, Massachusetts and a former student of the Fiction Writing Workshop at Columbia College Chicago. She received her B.A. in religion from Smith College and am is pursuing a Master of Divinity from Harvard Divinity School. Her work has appeared in over a dozen publications including *Steam Ticket, Fourteen Hills, Slipstream,* and *The Cape Rock*.

Nicole Rivera is a New York native, born and raised on the Lower East Side-- now known as 'The East Village'. Born into a multicultural family with indigenous roots, Nicole has struggled to find spaces for people of color, specifically mestizas, where she feels a sense of belonging. Most of her writing grapples with family dynamics and how identity informs interpersonal relationships. She studied Creative Writing in Hunter College before moving onto obtain her Master's in Secondary Education. She now teaches at a transfer high school in the Bronx, spreading her love for writing to any young person she encounters.

Anne Rundle's poetry has appeared or is forthcoming in *Artful Dodge* and *Common Threads*. She has a Master of Fine Arts from Ashland University. She taught high school English for seven years, but now works for a local community college. Her poem "Now the Teacher Becomes the Student" won the 2017 Ides of March contest. Anne resides in Westerville, Ohio.

Megan Schmid is a writer who currently lives in Pacifica, CA with her dog, Jack.

Contributor Notes

Jackie Sherbow is a writer and editor living in New York. Her poems have appeared or are forthcoming in *Okay Donkey, Moonchild Magazine, Bad Pony, Luna Luna, Day One, The Opiate*, and elsewhere, and have been part of the Emotive Fruition performance series. She works as an editor for two leading mystery-fiction magazines as well as *Newtown Literary*, the literary journal dedicated to the borough of Queens, NY.

Josh Smith has a career held together by spit, duct tape, and whimsy. No one else on Earth has both a Harvard education, and a pair of Iffy Awards for Best Hair.

Cindra Spencer lives in Colorado. She has an affinity for dark mysteries so she is often on the road inspecting health facilities. She occasionally dusts off her keyboard and pretends to be a writer.

Samantha Steiner is a visual artist whose paintings and drawings have garnered international acclaim. She holds a B.A. in Comparative Literature from Brown University. In 2017, she served as a Fulbright Scholar in Argentina.

J.B. Stone is an neurodiverse poet/fiction writer from Brooklyn, now residing in Buffalo. Stone is the author of *A Place Between Expired Dreams And Renewed Nightmares* (Ghost City Press 2018). Some of his work is featured and/or forthcoming in *Occulum, Riggwelter Press, Peach Mag, BlazeVOX, Mystic Blue Review, Breadcrumbs Magazine, Flash of Dark, Crack the Spine*, among several other publications. You can check out more of his work and other noteworthy updates at jaredbenjaminstone.com

An ex-actor, **Ben Tari** now finds his mojo in creating characters on the page rather than the stage. A schoolteacher by day, at night he writes screenplays, fiction and poetry.

Cash Myron Toklas is the pseudonym for an author, poet, and playwright who wishes to remain anonymous. He is new to literary publication, although three of his poems appeared recently in *The Piltdown Review*. His current project is a reboot of Hesiod's Theogony from the perspective of Saturn/Kronos. In general, his work explores the lessons that ancient myth can offer for modern life.

Lindsey Turner is a writer, designer, photographer, and nonprofiteer who lives in Nashville with her husband, son, and dog in a perpetual state of disarray. She likes to make things and tell stories. Her work has been published in *Shirley Magazine, Ghost City Press, Coffin Bell Journal, The Great and Secret Thing*, and *The Commercial Appeal*.

CONTRIBUTOR NOTES

Lauren Villa is a writer based in San Diego, California. She is a graduate of the Johns Hopkins Writing Seminars program. She likes to write about coffee shops, sex, space, and death. Her work has appeared in *Sky Island Journal*, *Thoughtful Dog*, and more.

Bernardo Villela has a BFA in Film from LIU Post. His first short film, *Suffer the Little Children*, won four awards at 13 festivals worldwide. He's since directed and edited short films, and a feature. He published a novella and three short story collections. www.miller-villela.com.

Andrew Weber is a freelance writer in Eugene, OR. He does a sci-fi webcomic called *Ion Grip* (iongrip.com), has written some fantasy novels, and produces a podcast of original short fiction called *Lies and Half-Truths*. You can see some of his portfolio at apweber.com.

Robin Wright lives in Southern Indiana. Her work has appeared in *Rue Scribe*, *Panoply*, *Terror House Magazine*, *Rune Bear*, *Another Way Round*, *Ariel Chart*, *Bindweed Magazine*, *Muddy River Poetry Review*, *Indiana Voice Journal*, *Peacock Journal*, and others. Two of her poems were published in the University of Southern Indiana's 50th anniversary anthology, *Time Present, Time Past*. *Panoply* has nominated one of her poems for a Pushcart Prize.

Emma Wynn teaches Philosophy & Religion, LGBTQ U.S. History, and Psychology at a boarding school in rural Connecticut. Her poetry is strongly influenced by her identity as a queer woman, a survivor of domestic abuse, and a Buddhist.

Jane Yolen's 380th published book is about to come out. She sends out poems to journals on a regular basis and has quite a few in sf/fantasy magazines as well. She is a Grand Master of SFPA (Science Fiction/Fantasy Poets of America), as well as a Grandmaster of SFWA and World Fantasy Assn. She has won the Nebula two times, Mythopoeic Award three times, and been nominated (but never won) for the Hugo several times. Six colleges & universities have given her honorary doctorates for her body of work.